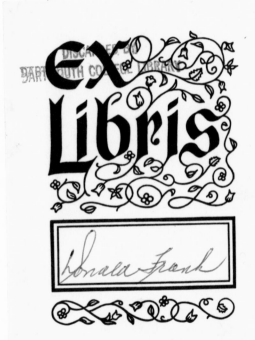

ex Libris

Donald Frank

ED FISHER'S
FIRST
FOLIO

THE MACMILLAN COMPANY
NEW YORK · CHICAGO
DALLAS · ATLANTA · SAN FRANCISCO
LONDON · MANILA
IN CANADA
BRETT-MACMILLAN LTD.
GALT, ONTARIO

ED FISHER'S

FIRST FOLIO

1959

THE MACMILLAN COMPANY · NEW YORK

The following cartoons are reprinted by kind permission of the proprietors of the periodicals listed below, in which the cartoons first appeared:

Harper's: pp. 46, 102 (1958)

Look: p. 62 (1958)

Punch: pp. 105 (1953); 8, 14, 34, 114, 119 (1954); 1, 5, 9, 11, 16, 21, 22, 23, 31, 55, 57, 64, 66, 71, 82, 87, 102, 104, 111, 118 (1955); 15, 16, 34, 45, 54, 65 (1956); 6, 18, 19, 25, 37, 39, 40, 41, 58, 59, 66, 67, 70, 101, 107 (1957); 9, 100, 119 (1958)

The Saturday Review: pp. 2, 42, 117 (1949); 98 (1952); 8, 11, 12, 21, 23, 32, 38, 42, 56, 71, 87, 99, 101, 103, 109 (1953); 2, 9, 12, 20, 24, 26, 27, 28, 29, 30, 33, 39, 44, 60, 67, 76, 96, 114 (1954); 2, 5, 11, 13, 34, 38, 48, 61, 62, 65, 75, 77, 81, 97, 99, 101, 105, 110, 111, 113, 115, 118 (1955); 15, 16, 17, 32, 33, 36, 43, 46, 54, 61, 63, 76, 77, 78, 80, 83, 85, 88, 103, 105, 112, 113 (1956); 1, 7, 26, 36, 47, 49, 53, 60, 69, 81, 84, 85, 98, 106, 108, 113 (1957); 6, 15, 17, 20, 22, 35, 44, 47, 50, 51, 52, 53, 68, 69, 73, 82, 84, 108, 121 (1958)

Sports Illustrated: pp. 106 (1956); 117 (1957)

This Week: p. 105 (1954)

Trump: pp. 29, 30, copyright 1957, HMH Publishing Co., Inc.

The following drawings originally appeared in *The New Yorker* and were copyrighted in the respective years shown by The New Yorker Magazine, Inc.: pp. 7 (1952); 10, 58, 72, 87, 90, 98 (1953); 20, 44, 69, 72, 88 (1954); 5, 18, 32, 37, 40, 49, 74, 81, 86, 89, 121 (1955); 4, 13, 14, 22, 24, 73, 97, 106, 108, 109, 111, 112, 116, 120 (1956); 3, 4, 48, 64, 80, 90, 108, 110 (1957); 42, 43, 51, 63, 106, 122 (1958)

First Printing

The Macmillan Company, New York
Brett-Macmillan Ltd., Galt, Ontario

Printed in the United States of America

Library of Congress catalog card number: 59-6981

ED FISHER'S
FIRST
FOLIO

CLEARANCE 12'5"

JEWELRY

APPRAISALS $2.00
AGONIZING REAPPRAISALS $5.00

Ed Fisher

"This story still seems unbelievable. Let's move it even *farther* South."

"More trouble in Little Rock! You'd think those people were being asked to send their children to school with Untouchables."

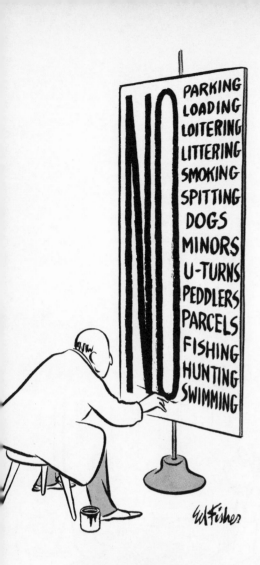

"Thanks, fellows—it was really quite easy. I made her a simple, unacceptable proposal; she countered by threatening to break off our relationship. I made it clear that in the eyes of all the neighbors *she* would seem to be the stubborn one; meanwhile, I stalled for time to let the vodka go to work; finally, I produced the marriage license. . . ."

"I don't know how you feel about it but I, personally, would just as soon go the *rest* of the way in on our own steam!"

"Pssst! Comrade! Everything's arranged: We'll supply paper, ink, penpoints, make contact with a publisher in the West, and split with you 60-40 per cent on all royalties."

"It's the most beautiful 'coming-to-terms-with-our-civilization' book I've ever read. I suggest we hold off publishing it until you've had a chance to do a few really devastating attacks on society. *Then* you can come to terms with it."

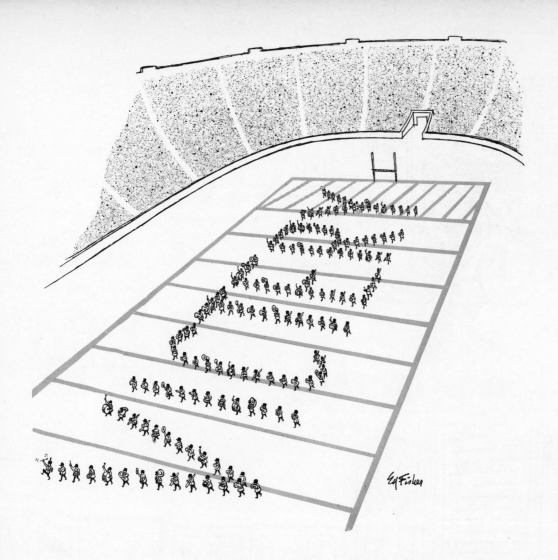

"It's the latest! Exhale, and it shoots poisoned arrows; inhale, and a special deodorant, concealed in the mouthpiece, sweetens your breath."

"Eureka, Mrs. Cluckhammer—I've worked out an arrangement
that will make your front room a distinct, unique projection
of your personality—diamond-pattern wallpaper, Degas prints,
breakfront bookcase, horseshoe couch, escritoire . . ."

"We'll have to let you go, Shandrov—those throbbing gypsy airs of yours make people too sad to eat."

"—Then, while they're still puzzling it out, I ride up and clobber them!"

"That? That's a place called Piltdown. Uninhabited."

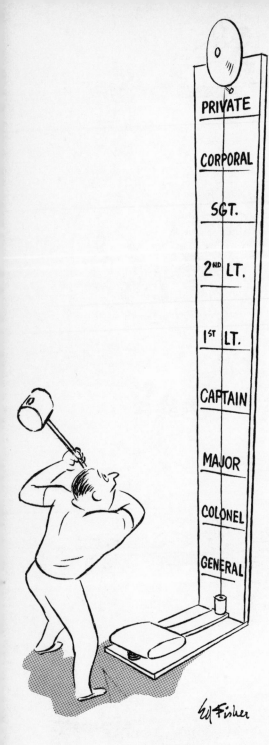

"What! Carrion again?"

"—Then, just about the time we had the spectroscope paid for, science suddenly went agog over the possibilities of the electron miscroscope. No sooner were we out of hock over *that* when we began hearing about the cyclotron. . . ."

"You're sick—neurotic!"

"It knew too much!"

"We're ruined I tell you. *It* was the only one
that understood the business!"

"IBM. Good morning."

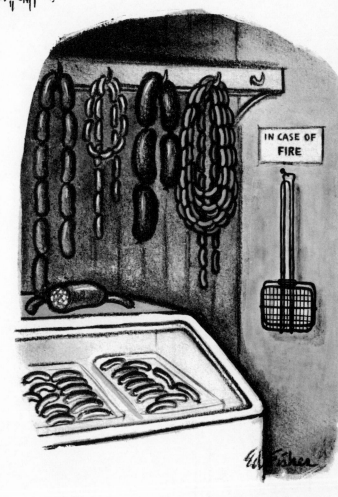

"How many times have I told you to trim off that ivy!"

"It's all your fault!"

"That's *you*, I suppose."

"Oh, that's Dumbrowswicz again—tremendous drive, no sense of direction."

"But I didn't *want* to by-pass Manhattan!"

"I started out as a mere printer's devil."

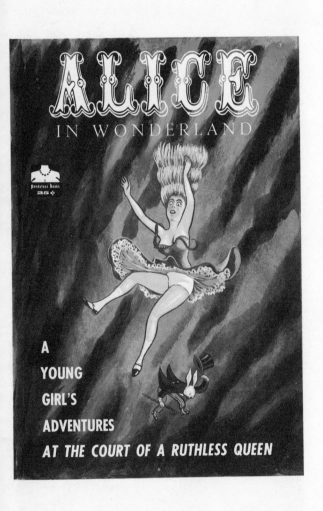

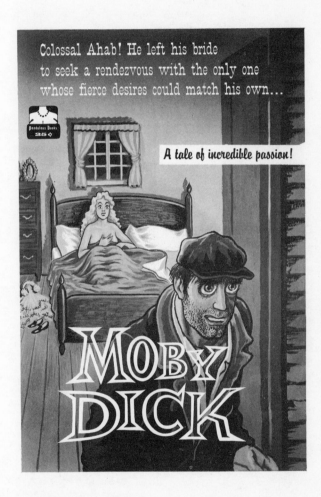

TANGLEWOOD TALES

by
NATHANIEL HAWTHORNE

...THEY CALLED HER "NAUGHTY PRIMROSE"
A BOOK EVERY PARENT SHOULD KNOW ABOUT!

25¢

THORSTEIN VEBLEN
THE THEORY OF THE LEISURE CLASS

AN ORGY OF CONSPICUOUS CONSUMPTION   25¢

OSWALD SPENGLER
THE DECLINE of the WEST

...HAD THE OLD TWO-FISTED BREED GONE SOFT FROM "EASY LIVIN'"?...A BOOK THAT'LL PACK A SUSTAINED WALLOP FOR EVERY RED-BLOODED FAN

25¢

LYTTON STRACHEY
Eminent Victorians

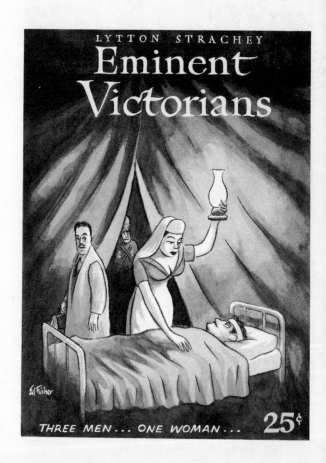

THREE MEN ... ONE WOMAN ...   25¢

28

THE ORIGIN OF SPECIES

CHARLES DARWIN

25¢

A SAVAGE
STRUGGLE FOR SURVIVAL

THE UPWARD JOURNEY

(ANABASIS)

XENOPHON ATHENIUS
Ph.D.

25¢

A startling, factual case history of
10,000 FRUSTRATED MEN
by the pioneer whose shrewd analysis
led them back along the path to health and safety.
Definitely a forerunner of the KINSEY REPORT

THE MEETING OF EAST AND WEST

by Charles F.S.C. Northup

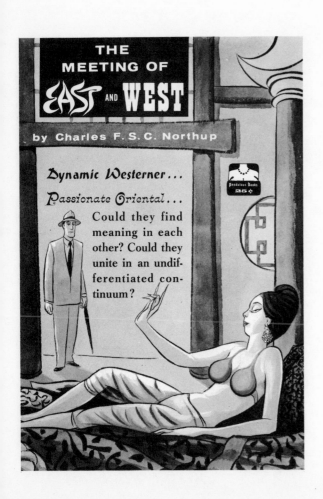

Dynamic Westerner...

Passionate Oriental...

Could they find meaning in each other? Could they unite in an undifferentiated continuum?

Pendulous Books
25¢

J. Fenimore Cooper
THE LAST OF THE MOHICANS

Pendulous Books
25¢

...THEY CALLED HIM
HAWKEYE...

29

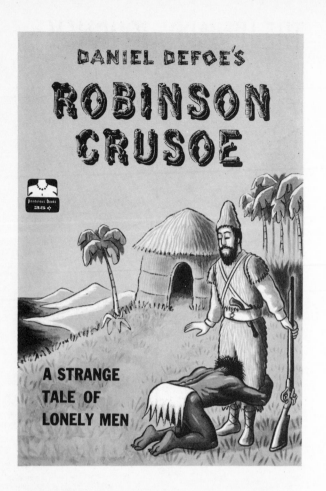

DANIEL DEFOE'S
ROBINSON CRUSOE

A STRANGE
TALE OF
LONELY MEN

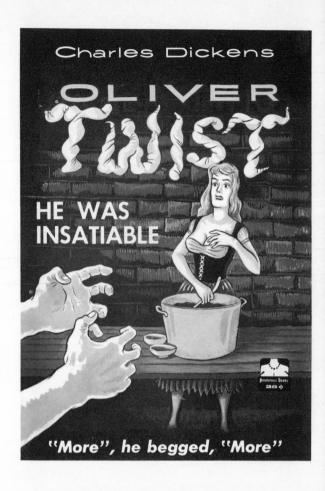

Charles Dickens
OLIVER TWIST

HE WAS
INSATIABLE

"More", he begged, "More"

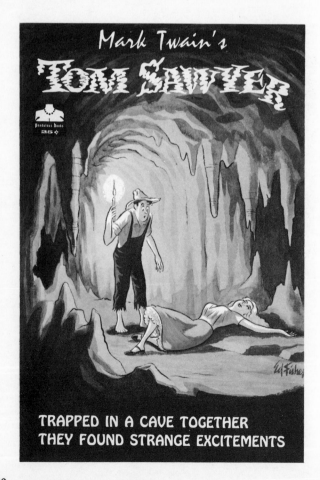

Mark Twain's
TOM SAWYER

TRAPPED IN A CAVE TOGETHER
THEY FOUND STRANGE EXCITEMENTS

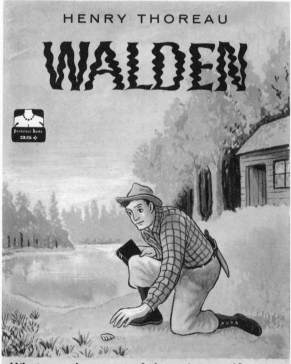

HENRY THOREAU
WALDEN

What was the secret of the quiet pond?
What could he learn from the lonely cabin?
An entirely different sleuth tackles one of the
GREATEST MYSTERIES OF ALL TIME!

30

"He would have wanted it this way."

"Thank goodness the preserves season is over—I've put up seventeen jars of raisins, twenty-two amphorae of corn, thirty-six jugs of oil, and forty pots of religious scrolls!"

"Okay—that's 32 lions. Would you care to try for 64?"

"We think your best bet is to try to get it read into the *Congressional Record*."

"Well, gentlemen, we've produced it—now let's see if we can cure it."

"No more audiences today. My feet are killing me."

"I can passively resist any man in the house!"

"How many men have we—not counting *Life* photographers?"

"I don't believe in it any more, either, but I think it's a beautiful old cultural ritual which should be preserved."

"He's telling about how we believe in the Sacred Hippopotamus who created Man out of oyster shells—don't ask me how he keeps a straight face!"

"Oh, he's a talented architect—it's just that, emotionally, he's never grown up."

"Shakespeare's got the right idea. People just want to be entertained."

"It's the hit of London and New York and it's about three or four people who live in a whole garret all to themselves and actually own an electric clothes-iron with which the wife presses her husband's innumerable shirts and they're constantly fighting amid this clutter of pots and pans, newspapers, food and tobacco, and the point of it seems to be that wealth can't buy happiness."

"You know, Eldridge, since you elected yourself a champion of the cause of Peaceful Coexistence you've been impossible to live with!"

"Someday all this will be run by atomic energy."

"I'm Detective-Sergeant Watts, Miss La Flam-
enwerf, and I couldn't help overhearing what
you said just now about not having a date
tonight."

"—And stay off Coca-Cola."

"This is Agent X5W. For heaven's sake send help!
President Gomez has been replaced by a twelve-man
military junta!"

"It was a rather close assassination attempt—two of the bullets went right through my epaulets and five through my hat."

"Good God, Senator—you've just started World War III!"

"Our country has been torn by too many of these bloodless coups— Let's shoot somebody!"

"They're not going to like this in Switzerland."

"Darling—the village blacksmith is having a sale . . ."

"But—first—a word about Government bonds!"

"Water!"

"AQUA!"

"Hydros!"

מַיִם

𒀀

𓈗

"I don't know what there is about it. I just get this feeling that if it works things'll never be the same around here!"

"Good grief! I've found a substitute for oil!"

"Well, Clambertson, a fine botch you've made of the Department of Rivers and Highways!"

"There goes Cheops."

"I never thought those California wines were *that* authentic!"

"Now, here's the plan. We let word out that we're in a state of political ferment. Russia smells an opportunity and makes overtures. The
West gets worried. *They* make overtures. Russia asks to send cultural
ambassadors, and we let them. The West asks for equal representation,
and we invite them. Then, when we've got them all here, we eat them."

"They're holding out for even *higher*-level negotiations—Zeus, Apollo, Hera, Mars . . ."

"You mean to say that you were his analyst for five years and never knew he was paying you out of Union funds?"

"Will you accept a deed, signed by Khrushchev himself, for five hundred acres on the moon?"

"What worries me is, if Adams gives it back to Goldfine and Goldfine gives it back to Macy's—will Macy's try to give it back to *us*?"

"Well, I certainly turned out to be the world's worst gadfly."

"Tell me about the old F. Scott Fitzgerald days again, Dad."

"I say! You don't suppose we've both been championing the honor of the same Lady, do you?"

"... And another glorious achievement of our Five Year Plan is that we all have twice as many ancestors to worship."

"Well, this is a little off the subject of Communism, but I'd like to make use of my immunity to admit that I committed the Roscoe Kearns murder of July, 1935."

"R, as in Right-Deviationary; I, as in Imperialistic-War-monger; B, as in Bourgeois-Internationalistic-Defection-ist . . ."

ANGLO-SAXON PLATITUDES
MEETING AN AMERICAN

"Like a little ice in it?"

"What d'you think of our Parliament—silly, isn't it?"

"Good morning, sir—still standin' it?"

magine you must feel like oman among the Athenians ."

"You know, if your State Department finds out you've been talking to people like me, you'll probably lose your passport."

"The vital decisions are all made in Washington. We're just a backwater; a charming, urbane, overcivilized backwater."

"The one *I* liked best is Margaret Mead."

"Cut that out!"

"A caustic soda."

"This is a paid political announcement: Folks, rats like me simply wouldn't be at large if you'd all go to the polls and elect Eldridge P. Schnurk District Attorney."

"Frankly, I'd have preferred a tax cut to public works."

"They say it's a battle for *our* minds!"

"We're here on what is known as a 'good-will visit.' I'm afraid shore leave for you men will be out of the question."

"I simply can't abide his 'more-Anti-Colonial-than-thou' attitude!"

"It's difficult to explain, I know, but after all these years of frantic spiritual turmoil, I've suddenly found solace in *this*!"

"So you see, Gruber, when you defected to the West, your Block Chairman, Pflugel here, was held responsible. . . . He defected, which was blamed on District Supervisor Kronk; so he defected, which was a black mark against Commissar Olinsky, which got him to come over; and this made my position at Headquarters so extremely awkward that . . ."

"Dr. Chedwick! To these people you represent America!"

"I'd hate to be president of the U.S.—They say it's too big a job for one man."

"And next year, probably, New York gets *our* May Day Parade."

"It looks like a stalemate. They're impregnable and we're invincible!"

"You can't tell me things were better than this when the Empire wasn't going downhill."

"Well, what did you expect? We come down here, hire 50,000 native extras, dress them in uniforms, drill them, arm them with flintlocks. . . . Why should they follow the script when they can take over the country?"

1.

"Rat! Squealer! Double-crosser!"

2.

3.

"Communist!"

"You'd make a good corporation president, cabinet member, attorney general or Supreme Court justice."

"Now, *that's* what I call negotiating from strength!"

"Say, I think I see where we went off. Isn't eight times seven fifty-six?"

"Deterrent? I thought you said nuclear detergent!"

"Son, this is the third fatted calf we've had to slay for you!
When are you going to settle down?"

"I know the world isn't ready for this yet—I'm shooting for the time it'll be unearthed."

"I've quit smoking."

"Of course, I never used to go to affairs like this until they started running them as Benefits."

"I've been trying to introduce a resolution putting this body on record as holding the idea of a part-time Presidency to be a threat to the orderly functioning of government—but we can't scrape up a quorum!"

"Hey! Where'd that *other* bump on the head come from?"

"I've decided to hand over control of the army and navy. It's a job for a younger man."

"It certainly gets harder each year to get any kind of a rise out of people."

"Man, we really *are* in the sticks!"

"What can I do, honey—it's three against one!"

"That Appleby always has all the luck!"

"... Just going in are producers Sol Harris and Maxwell Brent, socialites Whitney Ascott, Chauncey Weems IIIrd, the Duke and Duchess of Brixwell, glamorous Veronica Fife, Impresario S. Hurwit, Miss Brazil, Prince Alexei Orlov, and Doris Duvivier. Coming out are Brooks Atkinson, John Chapman, Walter Kerr, Richard Watts, Jr. . . ."

"The older people are all secret counterrevolutionaries; the youth are all secret counterrevolutionaries—that makes *us* some kind of lost generation, doesn't it?"

"Good Lord—you don't suppose *this* could be what's been fouling up the Republican party these last few years!"

"He's young, intelligent, ambitious—I decided to let him have a little more responsibility."

"The enemy won't even know what's hitting them—provided they're properly lined up, of course."

"Well, you were the one who said we shouldn't force religion on them—that they'd find it for themselves."

"Understand that I, personally, would have preferred to let the late, lamented Ozymandius, King of Kings, and his works endure forever. It's just that the political situation is forcing us to downgrade him a bit."

"I'll tell you one thing we're way ahead of the Russians at—Navajo pottery."

"You rang?"

"Gee, Og, it's nice, but isn't it awfully *big*?"

STRICTLY FROM BROADWAY

Memorable Moments from the Plays of a Few Seasons Past

"—What with that gangster brother of hers here for the weekend, and that insane artist in the guest room with his pet
baboon, and Lord Bargleigh picking this very day to call—is
it any wonder that Miss Emily is nearly frantic?"

"—And to all you ordinary, simple, everyday, beautiful people: a poet's cheers!"

"Ah—the lonely voice of morality!"

"O God, give me the strength for what I am about to do."

"Tom, I foresee dangers ahead for our nation—wars, inflation, demagoguery, race prejudice, cartels . . ."

"Here they come—thousands of them!"

"Genghiz, *darling!* . . ."

"Me! I'm responsible! Sure—me, you, the neighbors—all us shortsighted, money-grabbing fools, we're *all* responsible!"

"Father! . . ."

"—and now, a new string quartet, composed especially for stereophonic sound."

"For Jupiter's sake! Don't you think I've got anything better to do than drag you around after me?"

"Ten gallons?"

"Take it easy. You've got half an hour yet."

"I did it."

"Now, why didn't *I* think of that?"

"Don't just stand there—get the Nobel Prize Committee!"

"Hold everything—there goes a toadstool!"

"It's sinister. This year they send a pair of stolid, impassive observers—next year, from some secret training camp beyond the Urals . . ."

"—Come on—don't worry about *them*!"

"—And this is just a sample of the bold, youthful manner in which we could run I.G.&G. with the help of your proxy votes, Mrs. Hupple."

"London and Washington treat me with nothing but contempt, *Izvestia* calls me a 'feudalistic tyrant,' our customs are held up to the world as examples of barbarianism, we're in trouble with the U.N. Antislavery Commission—by Allah, we had better strike oil soon!"

"You have just heard the Second Brandenburg Concerto performed by the Pro Harmonia Antiqua Society under conditions similar to those prevailing at music festivals in the time of Bach."

"You're in charge here, I take it?"

"I forgot the message!"

"It's a fake!"

LOVE THY
NEIGHBOUR
FOR 10 DAYS
...IF NOT FULLY
CONVINCED,

"Who is he?"

"He was only a part-time Pharaoh."

"Must be that new bug that's going around."

"Actually, I'm just working my passage—it's part of the University of Salamanca Student Exchange Program."

"—And I've got quite a story for *Confidential*!"

"—And I'm the last statue
you'll ever carve. Promise?"

"—And then he promised to
get me into documentary films."

"This is my husband—he's in Automation."

"Men, Merlin here thinks that so many knights around one table is unwieldy, and suggests you'd all have a better chance to sound off individually if we split up into groups, with a spokesman from each to report the sense of the meeting to me."

"—Get them in either regular or Commissar size."

"Yes, but my Lord, Hopkins, where is it going to end?"

"I've tamed it!"

"—Of course, the Egyptians are too full of materialistic hustle and bustle to be *really* cultured. All they care anything about is size— the biggest pyramids, the fastest chariots, the tallest obelisks. . . ."

"Surely, Morton, you're not going to let a little dust on your trousers threaten our entire strategic position in the Far East."

"Bravo!"

"With all these, we certainly ought to be able to reduce our conventional forces, don't you think?"

"Another coalition Government."

"Sometimes these strange brooding spells of self-doubt and
artistic reorientation will go on for days—during which
time he can cook nothing but frankfurters!"

"—Figure it out for yourself: There are getting to be more and more of us. Saber-toothed tigers are getting scarcer and scarcer. Obviously in another few years the human race will have starved itself out of existence!"

"Sure enough! This one's missing!"

"Know what Ah miss? Ah miss that soft, sweet singing. That's what Ah miss."

"How about it, Don Pedro—a thousand pesetas just to shout an endorsement of Rodríguez' Wine during the 'moment of truth'?"

"Well, that settles it. There *was* intelligent life on Mars."

"Oh, nothing immediate—it's simply that in case of war I'm determined not to be caught unprepared."

"Course, there'll never be any place for *him* in the West."

"Sorry—I've changed my mind."

119

"You mean we're *all* T-men?"

"Little Nikita Khrushchev! How did he wangle an invitation?"

"It's such a *little* country. Couldn't we counteract Communism by just giving everyone a few shares of General Motors?"

"Well, *C'est la guerre*."

As I Saw It

A REVIEW OF OUR TIMES WITH 311 CARTOONS AND NOTES BY

D. R. FITZPATRICK

FOREWORD BY JOSEPH PULITZER

PROFILE BY THOMAS B. SHERMAN

Simon and Schuster · New York

1953

FIRST PRINTING

MANUFACTURED IN THE UNITED STATES OF AMERICA
PRINTED BY REEHL LITHO COMPANY, INC., N. Y.
BOUND BY AMERICAN BOOK-STRATFORD PRESS, INC., N. Y.

To My Wife
Lee Anna Fitzpatrick

Foreword

It has been my privilege as editor and publisher of the St. Louis Post-Dispatch to know and to work with Daniel R. Fitzpatrick for nearly forty years. It was in 1913 that he joined the Post-Dispatch as editorial cartoonist, having had only eight or nine months experience filling in as editorial cartoonist on the Chicago Daily News. More importantly, he had behind him a year of working his way through art school by ushering in theaters, carrying out dishes in cafeterias, and sweeping floors. Still more importantly, he had a full season as second cook aboard an ore-carrying freighter on the fierce and turbulent waters of the Great Lakes. It was these experiences which give him the right to say with solemn and unchallengeable sincerity, "I can sympathize with the underdog."

"Fitz," as we know him in the Post-Dispatch office, is a great cartoonist. Many competent critics in all parts of the world have called him the world's greatest cartoonist. I may be prejudiced in his favor, but there surely can be little doubt but that he ranks at or near the head of that great procession of men who have drawn pictures with a purpose, the purpose being to make things at least a little better in this great country of ours and in this distraught world. In that procession I would include Bush and Kirby of the old New York World, Davenport of the New York American, McCutcheon of the Chicago Tribune, Darling of the Des Moines Register and Tribune, better known as Ding, and the Berrymans, father and son, of the Washington Star.

The mention of these names requires explanation. For Fitzpatrick's style differs radically from that of any of them. Some used delicate pen and ink, in sharp contrast to Fitzpatrick's powerful and massive crayon. Others were content to show merely the whimsical side of life. Readers of this book, when they see the muscular forearms of Fitzpatrick's workers, or the brutal desk-thumping fists of his dictators, or when they see and hear the seas pounding and the winds shrieking, will agree that Fitz can draw; and when they see his droll elephants or his dejected donkeys, they will agree that Fitz can also amuse.

Again, his work differs from that of his contemporaries in the utter simplicity of the picture which meets the eye, with seldom a balloon, few, often no, labels, and nothing to distract attention from the editorial point which he is striving to make. As Thomas B. Sherman has well said in the following pages, "the whole process is one of distillation . . . economy of means is Fitzpatrick's distinguishing quality."

Fitz has been called a radical by those who have felt the pricks and slashes of his sharp crayon. When he is trying to help to eradicate a slum district, or open the gates of a slave labor camp, or expose a political stuffed shirt, or unmask a Secretary Fall or a Tom Pendergast, or take the hide off a Ku Klux Klanner, Fitz is an honest-to-God radical. But when it comes to helping the unfortunate victims of a great drouth, or a great flood, or a great tornado, Fitz reveals the compassion and the tenderness of a Florence Nightingale.

I trust I have not said too much. If I have, it is because of my deep affection and respect for this man and because of my great admiration for this great cartoonist, Daniel R. Fitzpatrick.

Joseph Pulitzer

vi

Profile of a Cartoonist

IN THE YEAR 1906 at the age of fifteen, Daniel R. Fitzpatrick took leave of formal learning. He had been attending Blaine High School in his home town of Superior, Wisconsin, and in three years of study had accumulated one and nine-tenths credits against a total of thirty needed for graduation. In the circumstances it is not surprising that the school authorities didn't take legal action to prevent his departure. The academic world wasn't through with Fitzpatrick, however.

Some forty-four years later he returned to Superior, by invitation, and delivered a commencement address at the Superior State College, not far from the scene of his early trials. On this occasion he was dressed in the gown and mortarboard he was entitled to wear as the recipient of an honorary doctorate of letters from Washington University, St. Louis, Missouri. His robes, to be sure, were not an explicit indicator of what he had done in the world, but they signified accomplishment just the same. For the lanky pink-haired adolescent who was innocent of geometry and impermeable to algebra had become one of the great editorial cartoonists of modern times. Superior, of course, now looked upon him as peculiarly its own, and the readers of the St. Louis *Post-Dispatch*, who followed his work from day to day, took a certain pride in the fact that here was a Midwesterner who had made an impact on the whole nation. He is a Midwesterner, to be sure, by preference as well as by birth, and as of now he has brought a measure of credit and fame to the midland region that few of its cultural representatives now living can equal. But there is nothing regional in his cartoons—no "barbaric yawp," no homespun sentiment, no stigmata that would distinguish him from an Eastern or a Southern artist. His distinction is of another kind.

As the collection of cartoons in this volume will show, Fitzpatrick is the universal artist in technique and intellectual viewpoint, but he is American too because his subjects are mostly American and his emotional responses have been conditioned by the pressure of the general life in this country. Each picture in the collection is a reflection of its particular hour in history, but when taken together each reinforces the others. The whole then is a vibrant record of two critical decades; and the body of his work, of which they are a part, constitutes a massive panorama of American life over the last generation.

Facing the school audience at Superior, Fitzpatrick was less conscious of his eminence than of the ironical aspect of his situation. Speaking in this spirit he told his fellow townsmen that his association with the Class of 1950 was appropriate because at the rate he had been going back in 1906 this would have been his graduating class. Two of his old teachers who happened to be in the audience may have thought that the joke was on them and that Fitzpatrick would have been even better off if he had never gone to school at all.

Fitzpatrick wouldn't have agreed. To this day he is still annoyed with the Blaine High School. He admits he was immune to mathematics. But history was different. He loved history and his love was starved out and left to die because it was never taught "with meaning."

"It was all statistics," he says. "Dates of famous battles, dates of Presidential elections, dates when kings had died and princes were born, and nothing much to explain why the great movements of history had occurred."

But if his curiosity about the meaning of events was frustrated during his early bouts with formal education it was never extinguished. The aggravating "why" that nagged his mind whenever he took a good look at the seeming disorganization of human affairs always forced him through and beyond the appearance of things. As a factor in his development as a cartoonist and in the daily practice of that calling today, the insistent search for the essence of a situation must be given equal value with his draftsmanship.

The idea or notion that is ultimately translated into a cartoon doesn't just pop into his head—or not usually. Guided by his knowledge of current events and their associations, he isolates what seems to be a promising subject and moves in for a closer scrutiny. Usually the subject, as first observed, is cluttered with details which must be hacked off, and the process of doing so is both manual and cerebral. As the pencil doodles over a plain piece of copy paper the mind closes around the nub of the matter or as Fitzpatrick himself would say:

"The whole process is one of distillation. All the mash of information and detail bubbles and boils around. The first run should disclose the subject. Then it is redistilled until its essence appears in a clear, simple draft."

Economy of means is Fitzpatrick's distinguishing quality. If one figure will express the meaning, two are never used. Captions are held to as few words as possible. As a result, the end product strikes the eye and mind of the observer with instantaneous effect. The newspaper reader, given a reasonable familiarity with the current state of the world, doesn't have to think twice if he's in a hurry. But unless he is unusually hurried or unusually obtuse he quickly realizes that the visible design stands for much more than it shows. Even the most restricted Fitzpatrick cartoon is full of implications and the best ones recapitulate a whole train of events and state a viewpoint.

Being a newspaper cartoonist Fitzpatrick is necessarily concerned with much that's topical and transitory. His process, though, is the process of art. It reworks the raw material of life and gives it a meaning. And that was what—unreasonably perhaps—he wanted his teachers to do with the amorphous stuff of history.

Fitzpatrick was not always the precise draftsman or the imaginative shepherd of ideas he now is, even though he cannot recall the time when he wasn't drawing pictures. The posters he made for school events in Superior, his contributions to the student paper, his impromptu classroom sketches and even the several drawings that were published by the Superior *Telegram* were remarkable only by a distinctly local standard. Nobody knew this better than Fitzpatrick. He had already made quite an exhaustive examination of drawings by professional cartoonists, or such as he could find in the Superior Public Library. As it happened, the library had an invaluable store of inspiration for an aspiring young cartoonist in the bound volumes of *Puck*, *Judge* and *Life*— the old prepictorial *Life*. They contained innumerable drawings by Grant Hamilton, Kepler,

James Montgomery Flagg, Charles Dana Gibson, Sullivant, Walt Kuhn, Eugene Zimmerman and other popular and famous artists of the day. Fitzpatrick was particularly impressed by the comic and political cartoons by Zimmerman, known to the public as Zim. Zim specialized in Irish and German immigrant characters and their garbled dialects—then a favored category of material with vaudeville performers as well as comic artist— and their vitality of movement and characterization delighted Fitzpatrick. In these and many other drawings he detected a correlation of idea and execution that he knew he didn't have. So he wasn't surprised when cartoonist Naughton, who worked on the *Herald* in nearby Duluth, told him he needed a "lot of training."

Meanwhile, Fitzpatrick was unconsciously storing up experiences that were to prove valuable to him in after years. During vacations he did odd jobs around the sash, door and molding plant owned by his father Patrick Fitzpatrick, worked as a machinist-helper at the Superior ship yard, spent a week in a Minnesota lumber camp and, in the summer following the severance of relations with the Blaine High School, shipped as second cook on the S.S. "Lynch," a six-hundred-foot, iron-ore carrier. The "Lynch" steamed back and forth through the Great Lakes from May until November. On one occasion, Fitzpatrick remembers, he substituted for one of the ship's firemen in the boiler room.

The net effect of his experiences as a manual laborer were several. Learning the use of tools, even rough tools, gave him an inner feeling for the coordination of mind and hand that he was later to apply in a more delicate way in clay modelling. He doesn't know whether it would be true for every artist, but in his case, he is certain, the manipulation of tools was a valuable early discipline. Then the close, repeated observation of men at work—seeing them shift their bodies to meet a certain stress or to apply the maximum strength to a quick thrust of the arms—was a laboratory demonstration in muscular articulation. And he also formed the habit of noting carefully the design and function of objects—stoves, fire boxes, winches, boilers, slicing bars and whatnot. With it all he was still an untrained fledgling when S.S. "Lynch" tied up for the winter.

He was certain of only two things: he was determined to be an editorial cartoonist and he needed a lot of training. His father and mother decided after a family council that he was worth the gamble; Patrick Fitzpatrick dug into his savings, and Dan took the train south to study at the Chicago Art Institute.

A northeast blizzard was sweeping along Michigan Boulevard when Fitzpatrick, suitcase in hand, arrived at the Art Institute and faced his future. The wind-driven snow was not nearly so chilling, however, as his early realization that each of the thousand or more students surrounding him was like himself—a neighborhood celebrity with no better mortgage on the future than was assured by the praise of the family circle and of friends who "couldn't draw a straight line."

Nevertheless he got what he came for. He got at the roots of pictorial composition by studying anatomy, working incessantly in life classes and drawing from memory. He joined the cartoon class. He verified what he had always known instinctively, that a sure feeling for anatomy was essential even for violent caricature since one couldn't exaggerate a face, for instance, without knowing the basic structure of the head and facial muscles.

At the end of his second term at the Art Institute, Fitzpatrick was on his own. Patrick Fitzpatrick was unable to finance any further study for his son, so Dan, in his third season at the Art Institute, supported himself by carrying out dishes at a cafeteria and ushering, at nights, at the Studebaker Theater. Meanwhile, he had been shooting drawings at the art editor of the Chicago *Daily News*. A number were accepted; and when a staff vacancy occurred, Fitzpatrick was given a job by L. D. Bradley, editoral cartoonist of the paper and head of the art department.

In the course of his stay on the *News*, Fitzpatrick did sports layouts, made thickly populated panel drawings illustrating the fads and foibles of the day and, in Bradley's absence, did his first professional work as an editorial cartoonist. Very little of the essential Fitzpatrick broke through during that trial period. For one thing, the *Daily News* and the general Chicago school of cartooning was committed to elaborate—if not fussy—pictorial effects and the free use of labels. Even then Fitzpatrick was groping toward a style that would place the heaviest possible burden of com-

munication on the picture itself. Then again Fitzpatrick was busy on a secondary level, storing up and classifying his impressions of the world and the forces at play in political and social movements.

He got a good close-up view of history-making when he was assigned to make sketches of important figures at the 1912 Republican Convention. His scrapbooks reveal an assortment of such figures—Judge Ben Lindsey, Vice President Fairbanks, Albert J. Beveridge and the volatile Teddy Roosevelt—all executed in the typical large-head-small-body style of the period. Fitzpatrick believes he must have been pretty naïve at the time. At any rate, he regarded the birth of the Bull Moose party—which split off from its parent body in what seemed a convulsive and world-shaking process of fission—as a prelude to a new, vital liberalism. He had no doubt that T. R. and his dedicated followers would "stand at Armageddon and battle for the Lord" until the last trump. Instead, and within a fairly short time, T. R. had maneuvered to a new position and his embattled followers were being described as "the lunatic fringe."

One of the most valuable aspects of his *News* experience came through his contact with Charles Dennis, the chief editor to whom he submitted his cartoon ideas. Dennis was an experienced, practical newspaperman but a man of broad scholarly tastes as well, and in his conversations with Dennis, Fitzpatrick learned something about placing the ideas that coursed through his mind against a broader perspective. Dennis, and others in the upper echelon at the *News*, served him as a sort of private college faculty. At least he was stimulated to do a lot of reading; and he rediscovered Shakespeare. Reading *Hamlet* as a voluntary act was unbelievably different from the imposed reading of the classroom. Shakespeare became entertainment. But despite the congeniality of the *News* office, Fitzpatrick decided that the *News*, for him, was a way station and not a terminal. An event that contributed to this decision was his temporary elevation to the post of editorial cartoonist during the protracted absence of L. D. Bradley. The chief cartoonist was away for nine months because of illness, and when he returned Fitzpatrick realized that he must return to the comic page, a prospect that he viewed dimly.

Moreover, he felt that he should be getting on with what he really wanted to do—editorial cartooning.

Consequently when one of his associates suggested that he write to George S. Johns, editor of the St. Louis *Post-Dispatch* editorial page, he did so promptly, enclosing samples of his work. Johns wired him to come down to St. Louis for a trial period. His acceptance proved to be the critical move of his career.

The remainder of the story could adequately be taken over at this point by a review of the Fitzpatrick cartoons that have appeared in the *Post-Dispatch* since and that have reinforced so many of its crusades. Footnotes are pertinent, however. If they add nothing to the substance of the tale, they at least can throw a sort of cross-illumination on the relationship between a vital individual and an equally vital institution.

THE OLD WOODEN COACH.

SEPTEMBER 7, 1913

First cartoon for the St. Louis Post-Dispatch *drawn at the age of twenty-two*

Not the least remarkable aspect of this relationship is that the unrelenting independence of each party toward the other has never been compromised even though their efforts have been almost continuously joined toward the same end. Beginning from the time, now vaguely identified, that Fitzpatrick earned his full rating as a *Post-Dispatch* regular, it was tacitly understood that he would never draw a cartoon that didn't represent his full conviction and the paper wouldn't publish one of which the management didn't approve. This understanding was ultimately written into a contract, merely as a precaution against unforseeable circumstances. The unspoken understanding, however, was given a test when the *Post-Dispatch* declared for Alfred Landon in the Presidential campaign of 1936.

Fitzpatrick promptly adverted to other subjects but no showdown occurred. Joseph Pulitzer, editor of the paper, took it for granted; and when the *Post-Dispatch* supported Thomas Dewey in the 1948 campaign, it was agreed beforehand that Fitzpatrick—who favored Truman—would take no part in the paper's campaign effort. It must be added that Joseph Pulitzer's attitude toward his editorial cartoonist was not dictated by a peculiar solicitude for a valuable asset. It extends to every *Post-Dispatch* employee who writes under his own name or whose personal conviction is likely to be involved in what he writes. Nobody is required to slight his conscience to keep his job.

The two Presidential campaigns were the two occasions when Fitzpatrick excused himself from a joint major effort. In the continuing effort of the *Post-Dispatch* to present the news fairly and thoroughly and to examine critically all activities affecting the public interest, Fitzpatrick has been a conspicuous day-by-day collaborator. Naturally his contributions have been most outstanding on occasions when the paper was throwing its weight behind a particular cause. In its nature the cartoon is an instrument of opinion and not a medium easily adapted to a balanced disclosure of a subject's every side. This has not prevented him from making amusing commentaries on current topics —such as the King of England's attachment for an American woman or the bickerings among the august personnel of the Supreme Court—in a way that invited everybody to join the fun. But there's no blinking the fact that his most memorable cartoons have been acidulous, opinionative and ironic.

A procession of Fitzpatrick's cartoons would be a reflection of forty years of history and a commentary on its heroes and malefactors. He has had his say about the Teapot Dome, the Veterans Bureau scandals, the entrance and exit of Prohibition, the Great Depression, Hitler, Mussolini, Stalin, Chamberlain, Huey Long, Pappy O'Daniel, the Five Percenters, the quick-money boys in Washington, and so on, and so on. To choose one or several from thousands would merely be to register an individual preference. A Fitzpatrick cartoon cannot be verbalized, anyhow, any more than a good joke can be explained.

The "Rat Alley" series deserves a detailed mention, however, for several reasons. In contrast to the majority of his cartoons each of this set has a "busy" composition containing a number of figures and plenty of movement. Each also echoes its predecessors and derives a part of its value from an accumulating momentum. Moreover, taken altogether they dramatize the nether world of shyster lawyers, touts, gamblers, blackmailers and thieves in a way that makes the series comparable to Hogarth's "Beer Street" and "Gin Lane." The series stands out in Fitzpatrick's mind, too. One of the sequences almost landed him in jail.

The first of the series was published on February 23, 1931, and grew out of a bank robbery. The burglars stole $822,000 in bonds from the Grand National Bank and sold them back through an intermediary for $125,000. The go-between, a lawyer and a member of the Missouri Legislature, received $15,000 for his services. He refused to divulge the names of his clients on the ground that it would violate a privileged and "sacred" relationship. The cartoon shows a grim edifice bearing a large sign which says: "St. Louis Thieves' Market—No Questions Asked," and in response thereto a file of sinister-looking characters are pouring into the entrance bearing their loot.

The general theme of the series, which continued off and on for years and is still subject to revival as needed, was the failure of the law to protect the community from a predatory alliance of shyster lawyers, crooked politicians and criminals.

The one that almost put Fitzpatrick in durance vile concerned a St. Louis character named John P. Nick, then head of the stagehands' union. Nick was brought before Circuit Judge Thomas J. Rowe, Jr., on a charge of extorting $10,000 from a group of motion picture theater owners. Even though a court of equity in judging the same case had ruled that Nick had received the money and must return it, Judge Rowe in the Criminal division threw the case out of court without letting it go to a jury. Nick was later convicted in the Federal Court and sent to the penitentiary.

Before that happened, however, the *Post-Dispatch* blasted the Judge with two editorials, and Fitzpatrick fell to with a cartoon entitled "Burlesque House in Rat Alley." The drawing showed a slum theater whose marquee announced the current attraction as "10 Grand Gone With the Wind." A loudspeaker shown overhead bawled out the words: "Ladies and Gents, the performance opens with the blessings of the law and the courts." Whereupon Judge Rowe cited the *Post-Dispatch* for constructive contempt of court and ordered the arrest of Fitzpatrick, Ralph Coghlan, editor of the editorial page, and Benjamin H. Reese, the managing editor. These three, together with Joseph Pulitzer, editor of the paper, who chose to represent the corporation, were haled into court.

Reese was released when it was shown that the news department was not involved in the alleged offense. The judge imposed a fine on the corporation and levied fines and jail sentences on Fitzpatrick and Coghlan. The latter two were held in technical custody. Fitzpatrick spent part of the afternoon in the sheriff's office in conversation with a deputy until bail could be arranged.

As Fitzpatrick learned during the court proceedings, Judge Rowe had placed a mark by his name, in a manner of speaking, even before the citation was issued. A *Post-Dispatch* reporter told him the Judge had said: "If that cartoonist ever puts me in Rat Alley I'll throw him in the can." The Judge was denied that satisfaction, as it happened. The case was finally thrown out by the Missouri Supreme Court.

Fitzpatrick has been accused, unofficially, of contempt and worse many times. The charge is usually made by his victims of the moment, or those who share their resentment. But while Fitzpatrick spends little time in melancholy regrets over the heads he has cracked or the flesh he has pierced, he is never punitive for his own sake. As an overall examination of his work will show he is usually striking at somebody who embodies what he regards as a wrong principle. As a matter of strict fact—which needs no psychoanalyst to discover—his basic emotion is compassion. This is often expressed quite directly, as in the cartoons of soup lines during the depression or the pathetic forced marches of Europe's refugees. Being so thoroughly aware of his own feelings, Fitzpatrick is a little surprised that anyone should accuse him of being habitually caustic.

"I was always for the underdog," he tells you.

As an explanation of what makes Fitzpatrick run, this has only one virtue. It shows his aversion to being permanently classified; it is also not quite true. As Fitzpatrick would admit, the underdog sometimes has rabies. A more explicit index to his temperament is his consistent reaction to pretentiousness. Even small and harmless pretenses annoy him and the big ones—the politician posing as a knight errant, the industrialist claiming that his sole reason for being in business is to provide employment, the artist who can't draw making a virtue of his modernism—affect him like personal insults. One of his most striking cartoons dealt with a meeting of Republican party national leaders at Springfield, Illinois, in June of 1935. The purpose of the meeting was to rejuvenate the party "at the grass roots" by reminding its members that it was still "the party of Abraham Lincoln." Lincoln's name was on everybody's lips; but from Fitzpatrick's point of view all the speakers were nothing more or less than the same old political reactionaries. In his cartoon the hall was crowded with portly figures and each one held a mask of Lincoln in front of his face.

Detecting a bogus attitude amounts to an instinct with Fitzpatrick, and he feels an equal certainty in recognizing its opposite. That his judgments are personal and subject to error need not be argued. In any case he would be just as fallible with an elaborate philosophical system rooted in Aristotle and Thomas Aquinas to support him. He is suspicious, in fact, of all formulae, including the fairly loose ones that guide modern political parties. So while he supported most of Franklin D. Roosevelt's social legislation

he was not an unreserved New Dealer. He opposed, for instance, the Roosevelt court-packing proposal; and while he sees many defects in the so-called capitalist economy, he is not enticed by dreams of a perfect society and least of all by dreams that must be realized with the aid of a machine gun and slave labor camps. What he relies on as guides to action, professional and private, are simple principles: the feelings as well as the rights of others should be respected; everybody is entitled to live a dignified life; men should be judged by their intrinsic qualities and not by their possessions or connections; it is an obligation of the strong to help the weak. These have many corollaries and the whole adds up to Fitzpatrick's Natural Law.

The satirical cartoon, as I have said, is better suited to attack than defense, and for that reason Fitzpatrick may appear to be more interested in exposing fraud than upholding benevolence. Actually a defensive and protective attitude is strongly implied. When he takes after fakes and characters who specialize in shoving people around, he identifies himself with their victims.

If Fitzpatrick's working philosophy is eclectic, in the sense of being drawn from many sources, much the same might be said of his technique as an artist. From the American cartoonists and comic artists who interested him in his earlier years Fitzpatrick passed on to an examination of the great masters. He was caught and held by the drawings of Goya, Forain, Daumier, Hogarth, Rembrandt's sketches and Doré's compositions.

His study of the great masters has been of inestimable value to him—and not merely in the personal exhilaration that it brought him. In observing how they solved various technical problems, his insight was sharpened and his vision enlarged. Without this experience and its results he is certain he would have been severely limited both in facility of drawing and in the flow of ideas.

The correlation of expression and concept can never be accurately analyzed, but from his own experience Fitzpatrick is convinced that they are mutually dependent. Greatness of conception is paralyzed at the source when the hand is not trained to externalize it readily in terms of a given medium; and to be balked even once in executing an idea sets up a psychological hazard. In brief, manual virtuosity influences to a certain extent the formation and growth of ideas. The study of great models is therefore both inspiring and instructive.

As an example of how a great craftsman can affect the work of a cartoonist, Fitzpatrick cites one of his drawings published in the *Post-Dispatch* of August 30, 1936, called "Toward Europe's Last Roundup." It shows great masses of soldiers converging in dense columns toward a man on horseback silhouetted on the horizon. A study of Doré's compositions taught him how to arrange the mass, give it a sense of movement, and how to give the whole a feeling of tragic fatality. But it doesn't resemble Doré.

The cartoonist, he feels, cannot afford to exclude himself from the field of the exalted and the solemn. Even the working journalist, especially in the present climate of the world, must be prepared to make comments in the most serious terms on the gravest, most far-reaching events. It is not enough, then, to command a skill that is only adequate for commonplace lampooning. So his advice to young aspiring cartoonists is always: know life and know the art of the great masters as thoroughly as you can.

Fitzpatrick regards the late Robert Minor, his predecessor on the *Post-Dispatch,* as one of the most powerful cartoonists ever to practice in the United States. He feels that Minor's surrender to communism was both a great personal tragedy and a loss to the graphic arts, since Minor abandoned his true vocation soon after he became a communist agitator. Any resemblance between Fitzpatrick and Minor may be attributed to the fact that both were devoted students of great art and hence were disciplined in bold solutions of technical problems. Fitzpatrick also admires greatly the work of the late Boardman Robinson, whom he considers a greater artist than Minor, in a formal sense, though not so strong a cartoonist.

During his first years in St. Louis, Fitzpatrick continued his studies by attending classes at the Washington University Art School. He did sculpture and painting; and he still paints whenever he gets the opportunity. The disciplines of all media have been helpful to his specialty. Working in color, he learned to translate color values into degrees of black and white. Clay modelling gave him a feeling for the third dimension and made it easier for him to suggest depth and thickness on a two-dimensional board.

Fitzpatrick's range in style is wider than is generally supposed by those who haven't gone through his output rather thoroughly and regard him as a symbolist, first and last. Discussing several of his drawings that appeared in *The History of American Graphic Humor,* William Murrow wrote:

> Daniel Fitzpatrick's stark, impressive cartoons seldom contain recognizable public men. Indeed he frequently omits the human figure altogether. When he does use a figure it is a sort of generalized Everyman and so it comes as a complete surprise to find that during the three-cornered wrangle between General Johnson, Father Coughlin and Senator Huey Long, Fitzpatrick drew extremely good caricatures of the three orators at the microphone.

Fitzpatrick also has a gift for portraiture—seldom exercised in line of duty—and once demonstrated it, as it were, under the gun. The occasion was his first and last meeting with his celebrated British colleague, David Low. The two met in a New York apartment hotel and an exchange of portraits was agreed on. Low started the proceedings and turned out a drawing that was both an excellent caricature and an identifiable likeness. The *Post-Dispatch* feature writer who attended the meeting to get a story took one look at Low's drawing and became a little apprehensive for the home team. He knew Fitzpatrick as an artist who dealt exaggeratedly in abstraction and was not certain, therefore, that he could produce something that would resemble the subject. He was surprised and relieved when he heard Low say: "Yes, yes, I congratulate you."

Fitzpatrick had undertaken a portrait without exaggeration. In his opinion Low was more like a Roman senator than the "little man" he used to exemplify himself in his cartoons. His drawing, in fact, was Low to the life, including, of course, his piratical eyebrows.

Fitzpatrick cartoons have been collected by print lovers, in St. Louis and elsewhere, and have been exhibited a number of times in museums. A selection was shown at the Galleries of Associated American Artists in New York during May, 1941, and again in April, 1946. A big Fitzpatrick show of war cartoons at the St. Louis Art Museum in 1941 was subsequently taken on tour. A permanent collection is on view at the State Historical Society of Missouri in Columbia, Missouri, and the University of Missouri sponsored a showing in 1951. Fitzpatrick cartoons have also adorned the walls of the Museum of Modern Western Art in Moscow. This was back in the 1930's however, when the Kremlin allowed its subjects free access to selected contemporary paintings such as those of Matisse and Gauguin. The French moderns dominated the Museum of Modern Western Art. Since then the Party has declared against "cosmopolitanism" and "bourgeois formalism" and Russia—the "Home of the Future"—and its satellites are the only countries in the world where experimental art cannot now be practised.

Fitzpatrick was awarded the Pulitzer prize in 1926 for a cartoon published the previous year called "The Laws of Moses and the Laws of Today." It was a comment on the multiplicity of statutes that had been put on the books in modern times and had particular reference to sumptuary legislation such as the prohibition law then in force. Since 1926 he has submitted no entries for any prize.

Fitzpatrick cartoons, naturally enough, are reproduced all over the world—in China, Africa, Poland, India, the Philippines, New Zealand, the Scandinavian countries—sometimes with translated captions, sometimes with the original ones. Fitzpatrick's subjects, even those who have been ridiculed, often ask him for the originals. Harry Truman was one of these and the cartoon he requested afterward became part of a White House collection.

The caption read: "No place for a kiddy car." It showed a collision between two mammoth trucks labelled Stark and Milligan, whom the political clockers regarded as the principal contenders in the Missouri race for the United States Senate in 1941. Truman, driving a midget jalopy, was trying to nose into the conflict. The midget won and was no longer a midget.

Before mailing the cartoon, Fitzpatrick added the words "Some Kiddy Car," and when Truman upset the augurs and soothsayers in 1948, Fitzpatrick sent him a wire that said: "It's still some kiddy car."

President Truman replied from Key West as follows:

> Your message of congratulations reminiscent of the good old days thrilled my soul. It warmed me more than wine. The trucks and their drivers are in the junk heap but the kiddie car is good for unlimited mileage on the rough road ahead. With affectionate regards,
>
> HARRY S. TRUMAN

In general Fitzpatrick makes little effort to improve his contacts with VIP's, possibly because he could be so denominated himself. A more compelling reason is the demanding nature of his schedule. Producing six or seven cartoons a week, in all but six weeks out of the year, leaves him with little time and less inclination for the cultivation of fellow celebrities. Moreover, he likes contrast in his leisure and he finds it in fishing, duck hunting, travel and an occasional session at the Twelfth Street Country Club, a loosely organized poker *Verein*.

Occasionally he interrupts his cartoon schedule —or rather he adds to his normal work day—by making black-and-white or colored drawings for sections of the paper other than the editorial page. For a while, too, he supplied illustrations for articles of opinion in *Collier's* Magazine. During the recent war he drew a series of posters for the Army Air Force at Randolph Field after studying the intensive, routine training to which the young

THE LAWS OF MOSES AND THE LAWS OF TODAY

APRIL 12, 1925

flyers were submitted. The purpose of the posters was to remind the trainees of basic disciplinary requirements, and toward that end they were displayed in locker rooms, lounges, and mess halls where they would be constantly in view. They were so arresting and so concise that they were subsequently posted at other training fields throughout the country.

This service gave Fitzpatrick a lift in more than a literal sense. During the First World War when he was of military age, he tried to enlist in both the Navy and the Marine Corps but was rejected because he was thirty-five pounds underweight. In 1942 he was not much heavier and twenty-five years older. So all he could donate to his country were his talent and his vacation time.

Back in the 1920's, when he had been on the *Post-Dispatch* scarcely ten years, he filled in for Rollin Kirby on the New York *World* during the vacation period for four successive summers. The New York *World* was no more militant than the *Post-Dispatch*, but he still regards his association with Frank Cobb, the imaginative, experienced crusading editor of the *World* editorial page, as an important contribution to his education as a journalist. The *World* was bursting with talent in those days. Three of the editorial writers, James Cain, Maxwell Anderson and Laurence Stallings, were soon to break out into a wider eminence. Anderson and Stallings were the co-authors of *What Price Glory*, still considered one of the greatest American plays. Claude Bowers, the historian and then an editorial writer on the *Evening World*, was also part of this group, as were Charles Merz and Arthur Krock, now with *The New York Times*, and Walter Lippmann, who succeeded Frank Cobb as editor of the *Morning World* editorial page.

Since 1913, however, when he first came to St. Louis, Fitzpatrick has been largely bound up with the *Post-Dispatch*. He never regarded this situation as a way station on the road to better things because there wasn't anything better from his point of view. It was inevitable that other publishers would make him offers. A cartoonist so widely reprinted could hardly escape such attentions. When the owner of a famous newspaper chain offered him a contract that would have yielded an income more than three times that of the salary he was getting, he reported the fact to

NO PLACE FOR A KIDDIE CAR

MARCH 29, 1940

Joseph Pulitzer with the following comment: "I'd rather work for you for half the amount." He got the half which in itself amounted to a handsome raise.

Fitzpatrick is not quixotic about money. He knows the value of a buck as well as the next man. It might be argued, in fact, that he knows it better than most because he knows what it can buy and what it can't. His compensation on the *Post-Dispatch* has always been appropriate to his value, but his responsibility for dependents plus his natural inclinations have held him to a fairly simple way of living. He never bought a car until he could pay for it in cash and support it. The profit motive has never influenced any of his decisions—except, perhaps, in a tough poker game when his blood was up. Certainly it was never a consideration that might have caused him to change his job. What he has centered on is the situation that affords him moral independence and stimulating associations. The trappings of wealth as such bore him or excite his derision.

Mrs. Fitzpatrick, the former Lee Anna Dressen, shares his interests and his disinclinations. They were married in Chicago when Fitzpatrick was a rookey on the *Daily News*. They have lived for many years now in a roomy, comfortable apartment in the West End of St. Louis. They have no children living.

The Fitzpatricks have a wide circle of friends and could easily have a wider one, since Fitz is one of the few international celebrities in these parts. Feeling no necessity to cultivate anybody for other than personal reasons, Fitzpatrick will gladly lift a glass with a bank president or a printer's devil, without prejudice, provided his vis-à-vis has something to say or, at the least, can ask appropriate questions.

In free-for-all conversations among his associates or anywhere Fitzpatrick speaks his mind and usually without lifting his voice. Those who are meeting him for the first time are likely to be impressed by a consistently ironical turn of speech that broadens into sarcasm as needed. This is a holdover, no doubt, from the habits of his working hours, when he searches for flaws in a situation or public figure. His associates have learned that this is no evidence of internal sourness. Though never exactly sweet, he is, you might say, fraternal and basically considerate.

Fitzpatrick, of course, is known to more people than he knows. Even so, the incidental and largely unsought contacts of a long career have netted him an extensive friendship or acquaintanceship with writers, artists, statesmen, Supreme Court justices, financiers, heads of state, and whatnot. The list would be fairly large if he had never left his office. Every notable visitor, local or foreign, who barges into the *Post-Dispatch* wants to see Fitzpatrick plain.

Fitzpatrick enjoys these visits; but he could do with fewer of them and particularly so if they come at a time when he's chasing an idea across a pad of copy paper. His co-workers, who see him tilted back in his chair with his feet on his desk, an improvised drawing board in his hand, and a larger board with Strathmore paper attached close by, always know that something's in the works.

After a while he walks out and shows the rough draft to Irving Dilliard, present editor of the editorial page. Everybody in range usually wants to take a look, including old hands who have been around for twenty years or more. It's one of the perquisites of working in the editorial room, and for Fitzpatrick it's one of the signs of approval he values most. Sometimes he will ask the office boy's opinion of a rough sketch if he thinks he has been aiming too high or is not clear enough.

At the age of sixty-two Fitzpatrick's inventiveness seems to have been stimulated anew by the shocks and surprises of a troubled world. His contributions to the 1952 Presidential campaign are among the most pungent and most illuminating pictorial criticisms of his career.

Like the editors of the *Post-Dispatch*, Fitzpatrick was favorably inclined toward the candidacy of Dwight D. Eisenhower in the preconvention stages of the campaign. Both changed their opinions after the nominations were made and each candidate had expressed himself on the issues. Fitzpatrick drew blood many times in the weeks that followed. A particularly successful cartoon in its combination of wit and lucidity dealt with the relationship between Eisenhower and Taft following their meeting at Morningside Heights. Taft, the Scout Master, was leading Ike through the woods by the hand and saying: "Chins up now and carry on."

In the heat of the campaign the public reaction followed party lines. And that was a pity too, because even considered objectively the Taft-Eisenhower cartoon was a model of expressiveness. Aside from the clear and vivid symbolical representation of the central idea, the expressions on the two men's faces—deftly and economically executed—were complete character studies.

Fitzpatrick shared the disappointment of the losers at the results of the election but felt no embarrassment and no regrets for his part in the fight. Readers who disagreed with him were often bitter in their denunciations, which was to be expected. Democratic partisans were proportionately delighted. But when the results were in and tempers had cooled, Fitzpatrick had lost none of his stature. That too was to be expected, because Fitzpatrick is valued for many reasons— for his political criticism, his craftsmanship and his art. In all three capacities he is one of the elected few to whom nobody can be exposed without being changed in some degree.

THOMAS B. SHERMAN

As I Saw It

Fitzpatrick

EDITORIAL CARTOONING is a sort of distilling process, as Tom Sherman has pointed out. For a considerable number of years I have been boiling situations down to a simple picture with a brief caption for newspaper readers. At the time of publication the current news background was available upon which these drawings were based. So much has happened in the world since 1935 when this collection starts, which older readers may have forgotten and younger readers did not experience, that some documentation is necessary, and that is one purpose of this text.

The operation of a cartoon distillery seems to be a mysterious process to most readers, judging by the questions I am asked. Most frequently the query is—who gives you your ideas? They seem to think some mysterious "brain trust" automatically furnishes cartoon ideas. Such has not been the case in my experience. Almost never do I get a complete, usable suggestion from readers or from my office associates. I often get subjects from my editor, but I work out the pictorial details. For example, if the editor is planning some special campaign or has some particular problem which he feels needs editorial treatment, he mentions it to me and I work out the picture. Ordinarily I dig up my own subjects, and that means keeping in close touch with current news events and considerable reading at home of books and magazines.

Meeting a daily deadline calls for quick thinking and rapid drawing even on days when news is slack and energy at low ebb.

A good basic training in drawing and composition is the first requirement. Working in oils and watercolors aids in black and white drawing. Modeling in clay or wax gives a feeling for solidity and adds to a knowledge of anatomy. This basic training comes before applying for a job, because a newspaper office is not a school and the cartoonist is expected to be able to handle his tools as expertly as the writer uses his typewriter. A working cartoonist, who lacked a thorough training in drawing, once told me he had many good ideas he had to pass up because he did not feel capable of drawing them. Too many young people feel cartooning is a trick to be learned in six easy lessons, and if they can draw at all or copy another drawing their friends and relatives rate them geniuses.

The modern crayon cartoon is an adaptation of the old lithograph method of Daumier and Gavarni. Instead of drawing on the stone, which wouldn't fit in with today's presses, a grained paper is used, and from it a zinc etching is made. Crayon is a quicker method than pen and ink, and time is of the essence in daily journalism.

My own day begins with my feet on my desk and a pad of copy paper on my lap. Sometimes the first very rough pencil sketch hits the mark, but more often I make several sketches which are pitched into the wastebasket. When I get what I want I show it to the editor; if he approves I make the finished drawing which is about fifteen by eighteen inches in size. I am not required to draw a cartoon involving a principle in which I do not believe, and, of course, the newspaper is not expected to publish a cartoon with which it is in disagreement. All of this adds up to a burden of responsibility for the cartoonist. For good or bad, the cartoon can be a powerful force, and in its very nature it is a critical instrument because in a broad sense its base is caricature and caricature is ridicule. It can also be adapted to varied uses. One day it can be gently humorous, which is often more deadly, or it can be a sixteen-inch gun blasting at a target. A former Attorney General of Missouri, who had appeared in some of my drawings, told one of my associates he could answer those editorial writers, but what could anyone do with that fellow who draws cartoons? The fellow who draws them often wonders, on bleak days, whether anyone ever looks at his work and the next day clippings may come to his desk of reprints from Australia or India. I have seen some of my cartoons reprinted in Chinese papers and the only word on the page I could read was my

THIS IS THE HOUSE THAT DIPLOMACY BUILT

APRIL 7, 1935

own signature. With such a weapon, and possibly a wide audience, the cartoonist should stop, look and listen before he launches an attack.

In the following pages incidents which arose in connection with some of the cartoons will be added to a brief outline of events at the time of publication.

In this connection it might be permissible to point out that this cartoon history was compiled day by day as the happenings occurred and the cartoonist did not have the benefit of hindsight. Looking back now at "The House that Diplomacy Built" gives that artificial structure an ominous significance since its corridors and pillars, erected by diplomatic barter and momentary political trading, eventually led to World War II.

1

HUEY LONG, the self-styled "Kingfish," with his slogan, "Every Man a King," built a political machine which is still a potent force in Louisiana. Heaven on earth was practically what Huey dangled before the "folks." A picturesque and to many a disturbing force, Long, a self-made man from the backwoods, fought his way up from scratch to practically dictatorial power as Governor and later as United States Senator. Possibly conditions in Louisiana called for a change, but the Long upheaval was another extreme with all the implications of dictatorship and its aroused passions which eventually resulted in his assassination.

In a speech in the Senate Long was once advocating some cause for which the *Post-Dispatch* was campaigning, and as he read from an editorial he paused to remark that he was sure the other Senators understood he had no great love for the *Post-Dispatch* in view of the cartoons they had published about him.

GOVERNMENT stepped into the economic picture during the Great Depression of the 1930's. To most of the younger generation, the Great Depression is one with the Great Flood and Noah's Ark. Unfortunately, many of the older generation seem to have forgotten some of its lessons and its implications.

The first step the Government took to alleviate conditions was under President Hoover, who launched the Reconstruction Finance Corporation to rescue banks, railroads and insurance companies. President Roosevelt introduced the National Recovery Administration as a blood transfusion for an ailing economy. The basic idea of N.R.A. was that, under Government supervision, Industry and Labor were to form committees to regulate prices, wages and other factors in an effort to promote recovery. The emblem of the N.R.A. was the famous blue eagle.

As the patient began to recover, he felt like kicking over the traces—if he could stand up. At this stage of recovery the nag still needed the support of the harness, but resented its restrictions.

"RIGHT THIS WAY, FOLKS!"

APRIL 14, 1935

**"ALL I NEEDED WAS TO HAVE
THE HARNESS LIFTED"**

JUNE 2, 1935

THE Republican party, which had been riding high in the days of prosperity, hit bottom when the depression came. Enlightened leaders of the party held a "grass-roots" convention at Springfield, Illinois, Lincoln's old bailiwick, complete with ceremonial masks, but nothing important came out of this show and they fooled no one but themselves.

AT THE GRASS-ROOTS CONVENTION
JUNE 11, 1935

Kansas City's political boss, Tom Pendergast, was a purely local character when these cartoons were drawn. When he moved into Missouri politics, he attracted the attention of the St. Louis *Post-Dispatch* on the opposite side of the state.

The long-standing fire insurance rate case was finally settled by a compromise deal passed by the Legislature. Huge funds were involved, and the pay-off to the boss resulted in a penitentiary sentence and the wrecking of the political machine.

The Pendergast Machine has since had more national fame because one of its protégés is Harry S. Truman.

Purely from a caricaturist's viewpoint, Boss Pendergast was the perfect model of a political boss and a welcome relief from public figures who look as if they were turned out on an assembly line.

WITH THE BLESSINGS OF BOSS PENDERGAST

JUNE 12, 1935

I'VE SELECTED THE NEXT GOVERNOR

OCTOBER 17, 1935

IT'S A BUSINESS LIKE ANYTHING ELSE
—Boss Pendergast

JUNE 29, 1936

FIGHTING FOR ITS LIFE

MARCH 31, 1939

7

WHAT DEPRESSION?

JULY 1, 1935

THE INDUSTRIAL potential of the German Ruhr Valley began to function again, and its production was not consumer goods. It was hoped the Versailles Treaty would keep the potentially strong German nation on a peaceful basis, but it didn't work out that way.

ONE OF OUR QUAINT IDEAS
ABOUT FOREIGN TRADE
JULY 8, 1935

ECONOMIC war quietly contributed its bit to world confusion and necessitated some peculiar actions in America.

The One World idea and the new position of the United States in its relation to other nations was not fully realized here at home, or if it was it was ignored by those who benefited by high tariff walls and crop destruction to maintain prices. Meanwhile, other less fortunate nations were on short rations but could not afford our prices.

WHAT COMES OF LIVING BEHIND A WALL
OCTOBER 1, 1935

9

SWASTIKA OVER GERMANY
SEPTEMBER 17, 1935

HITLER and his gang had gone a long way up from the Munich beer hall. The fantastic clown, not taken seriously in many quarters in his early days, had become a grim reality. How to portray the new movement in cartoon language? Perhaps this is a good example of the distilling process a cartoonist indulges in. The swastika, emblem of the movement, was modi-fied to depict the real nature of Nazism. It is pure pictorial language and as simple as a drawing by an early cave man.

Later, I transformed the swastika into a huge, tumbling engine of destruction which I used on a number of occasions. That conception came into more general use as other cartoonists applied it to Nazi activities.

CLIPPER SHIPS TO CHINA
NOVEMBER 23, 1935

Across the wide Pacific man's mechanical genius asserted itself. Inauguration of air service to Asia, a commonplace now, was hardly even a dream a few short years ago as history records time. It was a welcome cartoon subject because it gave an opportunity for a change of pace, something away from politics and rumors of war. The reader, if he had any imagination at all, might be transported from one great Clipper era to another with all the problems and implications fast travel and communication brought with it. The modern world was rapidly shrinking in size, due to such things as the new Clipper, so perhaps this cartoon isn't too far from the general subject of wars and politics, after all.

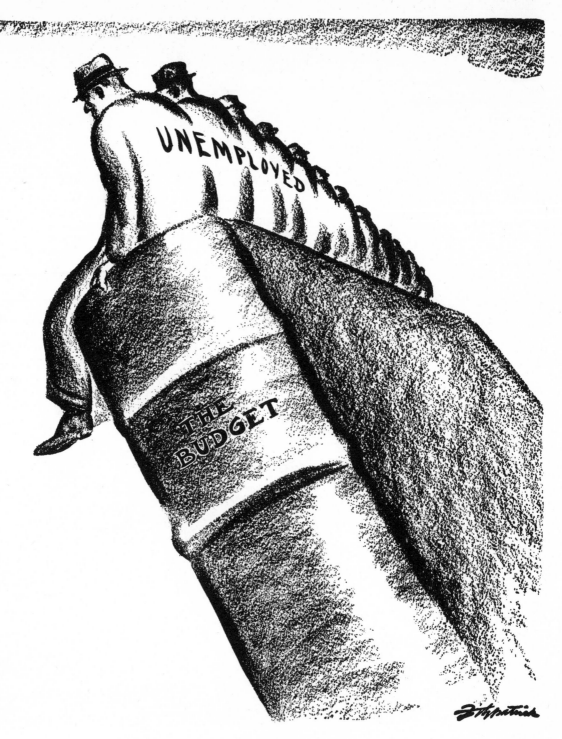

KEEPING IT OUT OF BALANCE
NOVEMBER 24, 1935

MAN's social and economic genius lagged behind. Spanning the Pacific by air demonstrated man's mechanical genius, but on the economic and social front things were not doing so well.

The Great Depression was still with us. Government aid had not yet solved the problem despite the huge sums for relief and "pump priming" which, it was hoped, would start the economy functioning again. This spending resulted in an unbalanced budget.

"IT SEEMS THERE WASN'T ANY DEPRESSION AT ALL!"
DECEMBER 18, 1935

"HOOVERVILLES" had grown up on the fringes of the large cities. Squatters' shacks were thrown together with scrap material by unemployed workers who had no money to pay rent.

President Coolidge expressed the philosophy of the Republican party when he said, "The business of the United States is business." President Roosevelt's reply was, "The welfare of the people is the business of the United States." Before the John Marshall Republican Club of St. Louis, after three years of President Roosevelt's New Deal, ex-President Hoover delivered a speech in which he indicated strongly that the "depression" was practically a figment of the imagination. The citizens pondered the question of fact or fiction.

SUPPORTED BY the Krupps and other powerful industrial groups who saw in Hitler's Nazi movement a chance to stage a comeback, the new German leader moved forward step by step, testing the reaction of the weak League of Nations and the war-weary people of Europe.

The swift, decisive movement of troops into the Rhineland removed Germany from cooperation in the Locarno Peace Pacts and destroyed the last military restrictions of the Versailles Treaty. Hitler also consolidated his position at home by a phony election in which no candidates appeared on the ballot except members of his National Socialist party. His junior partner, Mussolini, gobbled Ethiopia. The League of Nations took no action.

THE EMPTY JAIL

MARCH 8, 1936

THAT GERMAN ELECTION

MARCH 31, 1936

WHAT'S TO BE DONE ABOUT IT NOW?

MAY 10, 1936

THE WATCH ON THE RHINE

MAY 15, 1936

15

HISTORY SEEMED about to repeat itself. A new generation of Germans and French seemed headed for yesterday's trenches.

THE NEXT GENERATION

MARCH 10, 1936

IN THE 1936 Presidential campaign Alf Landon ran against Franklin Roosevelt. The accompanying cartoons tell the story of the race. Radio was a new important factor and President Roosevelt was a star performer. His famous "fireside chats" enabled him to address millions of voters without even leaving the White House.

BUILDING UP THE KANSAS COOLIDGE

MARCH 29, 1936

ALL BUILT UP AND READY FOR DELIVERY

JUNE 8, 1936

AERIAL BOMBARDMENT

OCTOBER 2, 1936

THE PAY-OFF

NOVEMBER 4, 1936

19

A SCATTERED DECK

MAY 19, 1936

THE Roosevelt New Deal, in its efforts to get the country back on its feet, found many of its major measures declared unconstitutional by the Supreme Court.

Frustrated by what he considered reactionary decisions by justices appointed for life terms, Mr. Roosevelt proposed enlarging the court with men of his own selection and presumably with his viewpoint. This court-packing scheme met with strong opposition and was defeated. A later cartoon (on page 32) will show how it all turned out.

THE GREAT DIVIDE
AUGUST 7, 1936

GROWING and changing industrial techniques of the machine age brought about a change in labor organization. The old idea of a separate union for each craft did not fit the needs of streamlined production. The new organization (Congress of Industrial Organizations) presented the idea which had prevailed in coal mining, where all workers belonged to one union. Instead of having several separate unions, some with possibly only one or two members, they all belonged to one union, the United Mine Workers.

Unionizing the giant steel industry served as the dividing wedge which put American Labor into two camps, the American Federation of Labor and the Congress of Industrial Organizations, better known as the A.F. of L. and the C.I.O.

SPECTATORS AT THE RINGSIDE
AUGUST 9, 1936

THE powers of the League of Nations, having failed to stop Mussolini's aggression in Ethiopia, watched a new aggression—and watched each other.

Lacking a strong world organization, and highly suspicious of each other, the European powers saw the "little world war" in Spain and wondered what it foretold.

THE OLD GRAY HOME,
SHE AIN'T WHAT SHE USED TO BE
AUGUST 25, 1936

THE SPIRIT of restlessness and adventure in America put the old homestead on wheels. Seeking new frontiers and opportunities, the trailer home began to crowd the highways of our vast land. They were the modern version of the old covered wagon of the early western migration.

This is an example of a cartoon not based on "spot" news but upon a general condition, and in this instance much depends on the caption. It often happens, in my own case at least, that I spend more time getting the right caption than I do on the actual drawing. The rolling landscape could be a Missouri scene, and it is the result of sketches and observations made around the state.

WHILE MANY Americans roved the highways in trailers, many more Europeans marched and countermarched. Men on horseback directed that ominous traffic.

TOWARD EUROPE'S LAST ROUND-UP?
AUGUST 30, 1936

23

AT THE TIME this cartoon was drawn the romance of Edward VIII, England's King, and Mrs. Wallis Simpson, an American woman from Baltimore, was in the gossip stage. But the rumors became stronger and the cartoonist's problem was what to do about it. Cupids and bows and arrows seemed too trite, and I thought it over for a day or two, discarding one rough sketch after another until I hit upon this one. The effort paid off because the cartoon was widely reprinted and so many requests for copies came to the office that a special edition of prints had to be run off. It seemed to be especially popular in England.

DIEU ET MON DROIT

"SO THEY SAY"

RETURN OF THE MOOR
OCTOBER 23, 1936

CIVIL WAR was in the air in Spain after the February, 1936, elections which gave the *Fronte Populare* a majority in the Cortes although they polled only forty-seven per cent of the total votes. The Cortes deposed President Zamora and elected Azana. Revolt broke out in Morocco and spread to the Spanish mainland. After a succession of governments, Largo Caballero formed a cabinet. General Franco, commander-in-chief of the insurgents, appointed a rival provisional government. Civil war followed with a bitterness that led to frightful atrocities on both sides. The hated Moors formed a part of Franco's forces.

SURVEYING EUROPE

NOVEMBER 22, 1936

I HEARD through our Washington Bureau that Russian Ambassador Oumansky regularly sent clips of American cartoons to the Kremlin in the diplomatic mail. It seems Stalin had an especial interest in cartoons, and I understand he admired this particular one.

The two characters in the drawing and the Napoleonic pose were well enough known to make the cartoon speak an international language. This might not have been possible with a more complicated picture which carried several labels in English and required translation.

WITH THE major powers preoccupied by European affairs, the Japanese took the opportunity to expand in Asia.

Manchuria was occupied, renamed Manchukuo, and a puppet government set up under Japanese control. All of China north of the Great Wall was being taken over while Generalissimo Chiang Kai-shek battled the Chinese communists. The weak League of Nations without American backing and with the European powers worried over events closer to home created a situation in Asia favorable for the Japanese militarists, and they took every advantage of it.

PIECE BY PIECE

JULY 30, 1937

"I THOUGHT I HEARD SOMEONE CALL ME"
OCTOBER 13, 1937

THE Great Divide, shown in the cartoon on Page 21, between industrial and craft unionism had thrown labor into two rival camps.

At various times, such as the one here illustrated, peace overtures were in the air but the principle that "in union there is strength" didn't seem to apply in this case and the two groups are still separate factions.

POLITICAL fortunes of the G.O.P. were at low ebb, and John D. M. Hamilton, National Committee Chairman, was having difficulty in finding a radio voice to compete with F.D.R.'s.

"CAN ANY OF YOU BOYS CROON?"
DECEMBER 13, 1937

ONE PERSON OUT OF EVERY TEN
JANUARY 16, 1938

THE fortunes of the American people were also at low ebb, but the Administration was trying to do something about it.

Following the philosophy of the Democratic Party that the "welfare of the people is the business of the United States," various Relief Projects were inaugurated such as Works Projects Administration (WPA). In other words,

Government stepped into the picture when industry failed to furnish employment. Public improvements of various kinds were undertaken, even such "make work" tasks as "leaf raking," all financed by Government funds.

The object of all this was public welfare and a bid for time to permit private industry to get back on its feet.

31

OLD FATHER TIME TAKES IT IN HIS STRIDE

JANUARY 18, 1938

IN HIS quarrel with the Supreme Court over declaring many of his recovery measures unconstitutional, Mr. Roosevelt had a strong ally. Through death and resignations, he eventually made a record number of appointments.

Thus the problem shown in the cartoon, "The Scattered Deck," on Page 20 was resolved, not by enlarging the Court, but by old Father Time. Decisions changed with the make-up of the Court.

32

RETREAT FROM CHATTANOOGA
JANUARY 25, 1938

BATTLING every inch of the way, the private power interests finally lost the war against the Tennessee Valley Authority.

The late Senator George W. Norris of Nebraska deserves great credit for carrying on a long, tough, thankless struggle in the public interest for the preservation of the Government's project at Muscle Shoals which enlarged into the control and development of the whole Tennessee Valley for the purposes of flood control, electric power and recreation. I am glad to say that the *Post-Dispatch* also carried on a long, able news and editorial campaign for the project. TVA has become a model of such over-all valley development, but the same forces which opposed it in the Tennessee Valley now oppose similar authorities in the other great river valleys.

33

"FELLOW DIPLOMATS—"
FEBRUARY 27, 1938

NAZI aggressions and ambitions having become clearer, diplomatic language became clearer.

Cartoon language also got down to fundamentals. It is, I think, a good example of the distilling process referred to earlier in which a situation is boiled down to its very essence.

34

We must reinterpret to the nation the political and economic philosophy with which the Republican Party faces the new circumstances of this new age. —DR. GLENN FRANK

MARCH 6, 1938

IN AN effort to revive G.O.P. political fortunes, the late Glenn Frank, then President of the University of Wisconsin, headed a committee which met at the Chicago Union League Club.

This cartoon must be looked at in the light of the realities of March, 1938, when the country was still struggling with unemployment.

The caption is much longer than I usually prefer, or am in the habit of using, but I felt it stated the case from the committee's viewpoint very well.

The setting of the stage in the luxury club where these important gentlemen met was as out of touch with reality as was their report.

35

EROSION ON THE EASTERN FRONT
MARCH 9, 1938

FARM-LAND erosion was only one erosion problem. The great boom and the great bust caused a lot of gulleys to form in Wall Street and "rugged individualism" was quoted low. Government regulation in the form of the Securities Exchange Commission was one result of the bust. Men's minds turned to the problem of periodic booms and busts and wondered how long America could afford such violent fluctuations.

36

THE MAN OF PEACE
APRIL 17, 1938

THE quiet Secretary of State from Tennessee, Cordell Hull, went his unspectacular way in a mad world.

The Hull trade agreements attempted to correct some of the mischief created by the tariff walls shown in the cartoons on Page 9.

In a world of armament and ill will with nations seeking new markets or new raw materials, by force if necessary, Secretary of State Hull's program of reciprocal trade agreements, for which he worked long and hard, was one constructive force.

WE WIN A PENNANT!

MAY 10, 1938

HOUSING was not a new problem in St. Louis. This cartoon was based on a report by United States Public Health Service which said overcrowding was the worst here of any city in the United States with a population of over five hundred thousand people. An English housing investigator said earlier our slums could only be compared to those in the back reaches of China and Poland.

But housing was not a St. Louis problem alone; it was a national problem, one into which the Federal Government finally had to move. This drawing resulted from sketches I had previously made of tenement districts.

A PROP AGAINST HUMAN EROSION
MAY 22, 1938

THE wastefulness of land erosion had become an important issue, and here I attempted to apply the erosion idea to the human field (and it was no easy drawing problem).

Our vast country and the growth of giant industries enlarged social problems to such proportions that local agencies were unable to cope with them. More and more it became necessary for the Federal Government to step into the picture as it did in this instance with a Minimum Wage and Hour Law.

This was one of the New Deal measures which caused a difference of opinion, and it is differences of opinion that make for the health and constructive vitality of our two-party political system.

WHAT NEXT?
SEPTEMBER 25, 1938

THE mere threat of Hitler's powerful military machine now seemed enough to carry out his ambitions. Success of the Austrian *Anschluss* and other lesser gains seemed only to whet the German dictator's appetite.

The next move was aimed at Czechoslovakia and the "rescue from foreign oppressors" of the Sudetenland Germans. Four columns of "Free Corps" troops of ten thousand men each, fully equipped with every kind of modern war material and under Sudeten German leadership, were drawn up on the German side of the Czech border.

This is an early example of the new characterization of the swastika emblem quite descriptive of its power and progress.

In the image: *This is my last territorial demand in Europe*

FOR HOW LONG?
SEPTEMBER 30, 1938

PRIME MINISTER Chamberlain of Britain and Premier Daladier of France swallowed their pride and went to Munich for a conference with the German dictator on the Czech crisis. Out of these negotiations came concessions to Hitler and the famous Chamberlain "Peace in our time." Hitler's pledge is shown in the cartoon written in sand, and while everyone was relieved that war had been averted, the cartoonist was skeptical.

EUROPE IS ALSO PAVED WITH GOOD INTENTIONS
OCTOBER 9, 1938

THIS cartoon is self-explanatory. Hitler's word was suspect in the previous drawing, "This is my last territorial demand in Europe," and the actions of the two dictators toward their treaty pledges spoke even louder than words.

Perhaps they both remembered that the Kaiser, when he invaded Belgium in World War I, said, "A treaty is a scrap of paper." These World War II leaders made "scrap paper" a wholesale business.

NEW RULER OF THE WORLD
OCTOBER 30, 1938

GERMAN air power, which had its tryout in Spain, faced the world with a new, swift destroyer.

From the old crates of World War I, airplanes had developed into a major factor in warfare and especially so under the German dictatorship.

This new military air power had its first practical demonstration in the destruction of the unfortified town of Guernica.

43

NO PLACE TO LAY OUR HEADS

NOVEMBER 11, 1938

NAZI ruthlessness was not confined to air power. Their talents were not restricted to new inventions. For the German Jews a long bitter night began as they became the "whipping boys" for the failures of the German "supermen" and their superior *Kultur*.

44

BEYOND THE PYRENEES LIES FRANCE
JANUARY 19, 1939

As THE "little world war" in Spain developed, it took on a new meaning across the border.

This cartoon proved later to be grimly prophetic, and it seems strange now that France and the other European powers failed to take steps for their own protection.

THIS drawing is included purely as a piece of Americana. A flour salesman named O'Daniel with a hillbilly band and a slogan, "Pass the Biscuits, Pappy," put on a spectacular campaign and was elected Governor of Texas.

It was a great exhibition of salesmanship, but just what the citizens of Texas got out of it was not clear to this observer. If any biscuits were passed around, the news wires failed to carry any such reports so far as I knew.

MORNING AFTER IN TEXAS
JANUARY 22, 1939

SIX MONTHS AFTER MUNICH
APRIL 4, 1939

SIX MONTHS after appeasing Hitler at Munich, Prime Minister Neville Chamberlain's hope for "peace in our time" vanished. Hitler's pledge, "This is my last territorial demand in Europe," was disappearing from the sand in which it was written in the cartoon on Page 41.

The Spanish Republic had been crushed, with Axis aid. The Sudeten and Austrian Germans had been reabsorbed into the Reich, and Hitler's troops, having marched into Bohemia and Moravia, took over Czechoslovakia despite the defense treaties of Britain, France and Russia.

Alarmed at the course of events, Mr. Chamberlain sought the cooperation of Russia, a World War I ally who had been shouldered out of the Munich deal, and announced to the world a new policy.

The Prime Minister's umbrella, which he carried to the Munich meeting with Hitler, became the cartoon symbol of appeasement. Now the umbrella was tossed overboard and Chamberlain announced that if the independence of Poland was threatened and if Poland defended herself, Britain would join in her defense. A line had been drawn—would Hitler march over it?

THE AXIS GOES ON A FORMAL BASIS
MAY 9, 1939

MUSSOLINI had been cooperating with Hitler for some time. Now the two dictators established the relationship on a formal basis by entering into a political and military alliance. The pretense of an independent Italy was ended and the accompanying cartoon illustrates the new arrangement and indicates who's who in the Axis.

POLAND, as Prime Minister Chamberlain suspected, became the next victim of the Nazi machine. The new technique of "lightning war," a part of which was tried out in Spain, was a swift, ruthless blow. The efficient, new, mechanized German army swept in and practically crushed Poland almost overnight. British and French help was too far away to be of any immediate practical use and a deal had been made with Moscow which removed the threat of attack from the east. With the fall of Poland an accomplished fact and the ruthless might of the Nazi military machine well advertised, Hitler scoffed at any organized opposition. His policy of "divide and conquer" had been too successful to be stopped now. Yet in a dispatch from Berlin Wallace R. Deuel wrote at that time, "The first phase of the European war drew to an end today with one single power the obvious victor, Soviet Russia."

NEXT!

AUGUST 24, 1939

MAD GAMBLE

SEPTEMBER 2, 1939

END OF ACT I

SEPTEMBER 20, 1939

TOWARD WHAT NEW FRONTIERS?

MAY 9, 1940

IT SEEMED LIKE A GOOD IDEA AT THE TIME
OCTOBER 22, 1939

HITLER's deal with Russia that "seemed like a good idea at the time" was not too good the morning after. When he and his new ally invaded Poland, he woke up to discover that Russia had grabbed two-thirds of its land and half of its population.

WHAT A PAL IS JOSEF
DECEMBER 3, 1939

HITLER'S vodka hangover in Poland extended to the Baltic states of Lithuania, Latvia and Estonia. His new pal had left Adolf out in the cold.

53

MISTAKES OF EUROPEAN POLITICIANS

EVERY TWENTY-FIVE YEARS?

SEPTEMBER 11, 1939

MEANWHILE, America wondered about her role in European affairs. President Wilson's valiant efforts at Versailles and his attempt to build an international organization to maintain order in the world met with opposition abroad and at home. The result was a weak League of Nations and a Europe described in the first cartoon in this collection as "The House that Diplomacy Built."

The settlements following World War I were all scraps of paper and America was reluctant to re-enter the European quarrels.

FINISHED A LOT OF THINGS THE LAST TIME
OCTOBER 27, 1939

THE invasion of Poland brought England and France into war. Although they could not come to the immediate defense of Poland, war against Germany was declared by both countries. The title of this cartoon, "Finished a lot of things the last time," referred to the changes World War I had brought about. The Hohen-zollerns, Hapsburgs and Romanoffs had lost their thrones, and the men who now sat in the seats of power—an ex-paperhanger, the son of a cobbler and the son of a blacksmith—were unknowns before that war. Now World War II had officially begun and what its results would be was anybody's guess.

55

RESETTLEMENT OF THE REICH
JANUARY 7, 1940

HITLER began to remold the world to his heart's desire. At no previous time in history had a ruthless dictator indulged in mass cruelty on so great a scale as did Hitler in carrying out his theories of racial superiority. Millions of people were driven from their homes in his resettlement program. Some 650,000 Ukrainians of German origin who had lived in Russia for generations were to be returned to the Fatherland; 700,000 more Germans were to be returned from Rumania, 600,000 from Hungary, 700,000 from Yugoslavia, 40,000 from Lithuania, 15,000 from Estonia, and 60,000 from Latvia. To make room for these newcomers, other hundreds of thousands were driven into exile.

BEYOND THE CHANNEL LIES ENGLAND
MAY 17, 1940

WHEN Hitler threw his dice in the great gamble for world power and launched his forces against the West, France was crushed, the British Army was driven to the sea and forced into the heroic retreat from Dunkirk. England now faced the threat of a Nazi invasion.

56

"FANCY MEETING YOU HERE, MR. LEWIS!"
JANUARY 25, 1940

REPUBLICAN John L. Lewis, who had strayed from the fold and contributed funds to the previous Roosevelt campaign, came out against the President and joined the Tory picket line.

The old saying, "politics makes strange bedfellows," seems to apply equally well to picket lines. In this instance Mr. Lewis' miners failed to follow his leadership.

RAT ALLEY almost landed its creator in jail.

Ralph Coghlan, at that time editor of the *Post-Dispatch* editorial page, and cartoonist Fitzpatrick were cited for contempt of court. All were fined and the two individuals were sentenced to jail by the late Circuit Judge Thomas J. Rowe, Jr. This was for publishing two editorials and a Rat Alley cartoon which were inspired by the fact that Judge Rowe dismissed a criminal case without even calling a jury, while in another Circuit Court, Judge Oakley, trying the civil phase of the same case, said the defendants were guilty and must restore the ten thousand dollars which they were charged with extorting from local movie theater operators.

The Federal Court a few months later sent the racketeers to the penitentiary on the same criminal charge.

The Missouri Supreme Court overruled Judge Rowe on the contempt case and the editor and cartoonist escaped jail.

BURLESQUE HOUSE IN RAT ALLEY

MARCH 6, 1940

A THREAT AS OLD AS DEMOCRACY

APRIL 4, 1940

**BURLESQUE HOUSE IN RAT ALLEY
AFTER UNCLE SAM'S VISIT**

SEPTEMBER 20, 1940

THE LAST WORD

JUNE 11, 1941

THE *Post-Dispatch* conducted a notable and successful campaign against the smoke evil which had all but ruined St. Louis as a place to live. Low-grade Illinois coal was available just across the river. Higher-grade coal had to be hauled from greater distances, which added more to the cost of heat, especially for consumers least able to pay. And this was only one of the smoke elimination problems. Whole communities on the Illinois side, where the chief industry was coal mining, threatened to boycott St. Louis department stores which advertised in the *Post-Dispatch*. This was intended to stop the news and editorial campaign, but it didn't work out that way. St. Louis had suffered too long from the smoke blight, and the city's future growth was at stake. James L. Ford, Jr., headed a citizens' committee which solved most of the technical and economic problems, such as furnace alterations, to make low-grade coal usable. The newspaper and the committee carried on the fight until the antismoke ordinance became law.

START OF THE BIG PUSH
MARCH 21, 1940

HOW DID YOU MANAGE TO QUIT SMOKING?
DECEMBER 21, 1940

"MY SONS, LOOK TO OUR DEFENSES"
MAY 26, 1940

THE warning of events became clearer on this side of the Atlantic. Hitler's plans had been made plain in his book, *Mein Kampf,* but they were so fantastic no one took that warning too seriously until he had demonstrated his ruthlessness in herding whole populations from their homes in mass migrations and his military power in crushing all opposition in Western Europe.

The Atlantic was no longer a protecting barrier in this age of submarines and airplanes. America's relation with the world and especially with Europe needed to be brought into line with realities.

"IT IS MY WISH"
JUNE 11, 1940

ON JUNE 10, 1940, Mussolini declared war. The Italian dictator, after playing coy in the international chess game, thought he saw an opportunity. Hitler's mechanized forces moved west. The Nazi machine crushed France and the French-Italian war lasted just sixteen days. Military experts still debate the value of Mussolini's contribution to the victory. Italian troops broke the line of fortifications on the French-Italian border and penetrated five to twenty miles into French territory.

Italy was awarded the scant French territory she had gained, plus a demilitarized zone in Tunisia and a demilitarized French Somaliland. Mussolini's next Axis contribution was expected to be an attack on Suez. The British Navy took care of that phase of the Italian dictator's ambitions.

"WE FEARED YOU MORE THAN WE FEARED HITLER"

JULY 2, 1940

THE reactionary forces in France played the game of the invader. The aged hero of World War I, Marshal Petain, became head of the so-called Vichy Government with Pierre Laval as Premier. Collaboration became the watchword, and the German Nazis ruled France, with their own troops in Paris and the north and the Vichy collaborators in the South.

SPECIAL
RELIEF
SESSION

MISSOURI'S OWN REFUGEES
JULY 23, 1940

IF THIS collection of cartoons abruptly refers to some purely American or strictly local subject, it is because such items were important at the time. In this particular instance the cartoon is of enough general interest to be understood almost anywhere.

This Missouri subject reminds me of the filing system our Jefferson City correspondent, Boyd Carroll, devised. Every cartoon of mine pertaining to state government was pasted on the office walls. Whenever Boyd wrote a story, all he did to refresh his memory was to glance at the cartoon clips on the walls. Unfortunately, the system was disrupted when the office was moved, so the new files were started on movable screens.

65

In England conditions were far worse with German air power exerting its might. The new force was asserting itself against civilian as well as military targets. No longer was the Channel a moat of protection for England. Control of the sea had been England's potent weapon for so many years it was difficult to reorient one's thoughts to air attack.

THE WORLD OF TOMORROW
SEPTEMBER 29, 1940

1940 was Presidential election year in America. Wendell L. Willkie ran as the Republican candidate against Franklin D. Roosevelt. There was no doubt as to who the Democratic candidate would be, as the cartoon of July 12, 1940, shows. The Republican Convention was stampeded by supporters of Wendell L. Willkie, a newcomer in the political field, who represented the liberal Republican viewpoint and won the nomination.

ONE FACTORY REOPENED

MAY 9, 1938

AWAITING HIS MASTER

JULY 12, 1940

END OF THE SHADOWBOXING

OCTOBER 22, 1940

"TO THE PRESIDENT OF THE UNITED STATES"

NOVEMBER 6, 1940

THIS IS a local Missouri cartoon, but it is included because Missouri politics have moved into the national field. The late Lawrence McDaniel, Democratic candidate for Governor in 1940, was defeated by Forrest Donnell by the narrow margin of three thousand, six hundred and thirteen votes. The Democrats, who controlled the State Legislature, attempted to steal the governorship for their man. The machine backing McDaniel was headed by the late Robert E. Hannegan, later Postmaster General, and as a result of the governorship steal the organization lost the St. Louis City election. The net result was the loss of the patronage of both the Governor's office and that of the Mayor of St. Louis. However, some of the top strategists went on to bigger and better things through Federal patronage.

COME ON IN, LARRY, THE RACE IS OVER
NOVEMBER 18, 1940

THE NEW ORDER IN RUMANIA
NOVEMBER 28, 1940

KING CAROL of Rumania, shortly before he abdicated the throne in favor of his son, named General Ion Antonescu Premier with practically dictatorial powers. His force, known as the "Iron Guard," proceeded to avenge the execution of its former leaders. A week of massacres and terrorism swept the country. Sixty-four leading dignitaries were executed. On November 23, 1940, Premier-General Antonescu signed a protocol joining the Axis.

FRENCH "LEBENSRAUM"

DECEMBER 2, 1940

HITLER'S ruthlessness together with the collaboration of French reactionaries reduced the French people to a position of servitude.

Raw physical power erased the old French motto of *Liberté, Egalité, Fraternité,* and the goose-steppers marched on the boulevards of Paris.

Lebensraum, Hitler's rallying slogan for living room for the Germans, became something else for the French people.

73

PROBLEM BEFORE THE CONGRESS
JANUARY 7, 1941

MEANWHILE, America, and especially members of Congress responsible for decisions in the international field, weighed our relationship to the march of dictatorship in Europe with deep memories of our previous intervention in World War I.

74

THE ROAD AHEAD
MARCH 18, 1941

"THE ROAD AHEAD" was not an easy road for America. Mr. Churchill's "blood, toil, tears and sweat" trail appeared to be America's route. This cartoon is based upon a speech by President Roosevelt.

All-out aid to Britain had been granted under the Lend-Lease Act, and an appropriation of seven billion dollars to finance the Act had been requested. This, plus the most sweeping powers granted to the President, followed a long series of events by which the country had gradually moved from neutrality to non-shooting intervention. This pattern meant only one thing.

MUSSOLINI's pretentions had by now caught up with him. Hitler's superior military power had long since relegated the junior Axis partner to a position of flunky to his German master. Military necessity forced the Germans into Italy. The Italian people hated the Germans and the Germans despised the Italians. As a result, Italy became in fact occupied German territory.

THE GRANDEUR THAT WAS ROME
APRIL 12, 1941

75

SOCIETY ITEM
JULY 9, 1941

FORGETTING what happened to Napoleon, Hitler, who still was unable to cross the English Channel, turned his war machine on his erstwhile ally, Russia. As a victim of Nazi aggression and a potent ally, Russia was promptly and politely welcomed to the anti-Axis side in a fateful radio address from London by Prime Minister Churchill.

FROM THE BALTIC TO THE BLACK
AUGUST 24, 1941

THE European land war became a test of strength between the efficient German war machine and Russian manpower. The Allied naval blockade plus the aid of American factories, which supplied the Russian armies, built up a force which first checked and then stopped the Nazis on the long line from the Baltic to the Black Sea.

THE SHOOTING WAR HAS STARTED—President Roosevelt

NOVEMBER 1, 1941

The desperate Nazi submarine warfare for all practical purposes involved us. The American destroyer, "Reuben James," on convoy duty in the North Atlantic west of Iceland, was sunk by a Nazi U-boat. One hundred and one men perished; forty-nine were saved, including eight wounded.

This was the third encounter American destroyers on convoy duty had had with German submarines. On September 4, 1941, two torpedoes were fired at the "Greer" but they failed to hit the target. On the night of October 16-17, 1941, the "Kearney" was hit when it left its own convoy to aid another which was under attack. Eleven American sailors were killed. The shooting war had started.

THE ASSASSIN STRIKES
DECEMBER 8, 1941

THE Japanese attack on Pearl Harbor formally opened the Axis struggle with America.

What happened on that occasion has been fully explored and the facts have been widely published. News of the attack reached me at home Sunday afternoon by radio, and I imme- diately went to the office which was practically deserted, since we are an afternoon newspaper. The whole story had not come in, but enough news had arrived to make it plain that this was it. On the basis of those early reports, I drew this cartoon for the next day's paper.

WAIT TILL HE LEARNS WHAT HE'S GOT HOLD OF
DECEMBER 28, 1941

WITH the preponderance of Allied strength concentrated in the European theater, plus United States naval losses at Pearl Harbor, the Japanese had a comparatively clear field in which to operate in the Pacific and Asia. But early gains were deceiving as the Japanese were to learn later after the United States had mobilized its full power.

WE WON'T FORGET
APRIL 10, 1942

WE LOST the second round in the Pacific war. General MacArthur had been ordered by President Roosevelt to leave the Philippines and proceed to Australia for the purpose of rebuilding Allied forces for a counterattack.

Bataan, our besieged fortress in Manila Bay, surrendered. The Japanese military machine had piled up a swift series of conquests in Asia following its sneak attack on Pearl Harbor.

Two of Britain's largest battleships, the "Repulse" and the "Prince of Wales" had been sunk by Japanese planes. The American islands of Wake and Guam had been occupied and Hong Kong and Singapore had fallen. Defense of the Malay Peninsula was abandoned, and the victorious Japanese were advancing into Burma and the Dutch East Indies. But, all this was only the end of round two.

"HI, TOOTS!"
APRIL 30, 1942

WARTIME rationing restrictions at home at least furnished material for a lighter touch in cartoons. Most of the war news at this time was much too grim for humorous treatment, but humor, when it could be found, was a release from tension. Sugar was already on the ration shelf and when tires were put there, sweetie had a companion.

82

"FRENCHMEN, I BESPEAK THE NEW ORDER"
JUNE 28, 1942

THIS WAS what was happening in the land of Voltaire and Lafayette. Pierre Laval, collaborationist tool of the Nazis in France, played the German game while others of his countrymen risked their necks in the Underground resistance movement.

Cartoonwise, the Nazi swastika lent itself to a new treatment.

THERE WERE new rounds in the Pacific fight. In the battle of Midway all damage was exclusively from air and submarine action, and no surface vessels exchanged fire. The Japanese lost four carriers, two cruisers and three destroyers. Three battleships, four cruisers and a number of lighter craft were damaged. An estimated two hundred and seventy-five Japanese planes were knocked down. The United States carrier "Yorktown" and one destroyer were lost. American casualties were three hundred and seven officers and men. No plane losses were given. Midway was a decisive Allied victory because it halted a major Japanese effort to capture Midway and destroy the United States Pacific fleet.

In the Bismarck Sea battle, United States land-based bombers destroyed an entire convoy of ten warships and twelve transports that was caught off the coast of New Britain. This action crushed Japanese hopes of reconquering the Huon Gulf area. In both cartoons the rising sun design of the Japanese flag was utilized as a cartoon symbol.

THE RISING SUN AT MIDWAY

JULY 16, 1942

OIL SLICK ON THE BISMARCK SEA

MARCH 5, 1943

EVIDENCE IS BEING RELENTLESSLY PILED UP—President Roosevelt

OCTOBER 16, 1942

Nazi ruthlessness had its warning from President Roosevelt in his statement, "Evidence is being relentlessly piled up." The leaders who instigated civilian mass murders were being notified that war guilt is personal. War in this instance took on a different meaning.

Earlier wars were conducted by uniformed armies of the contending nations, and a hapless civilian population was only incidentally involved.

The Nazis changed that system and the warrior, with a background of King Arthur and his knights, became a butcher of civilians with the code of the modern gangster.

GATEWAY TO STALINGRAD
NOVEMBER 25, 1942

THE Russian defense of Stalingrad was breaking the backbone of the mighty *panzer* machine. The German drive on Stalingrad was aimed at separating the Russian armies in the Caucasus from the northern armies, thus gaining control of the Volga river, a vital artery of transport. Russian armies would then have been forced to retreat to the river's east bank. The battle began August 22-24 and in the final push forty divisions with armored forces and one thousand planes were hurled against the defenders. Few buildings were left standing, but every ruined house and rubble pile became a defense pillbox. German casualties in two months amounted to 900,000. Loss of material was equally great.

The Nazi machine had suffered a major defeat.

RUMBLING DOWN UNDER
DECEMBER 3, 1942

IN Italy the Facist regime faced revolt. The Italian people were held in line by what amounted to German military occupation. Allied leaders meeting at Casablanca made known their terms to the Axis powers.

TERMS FROM CASABLANCA
JANUARY 28, 1943

THE ROAD BACK
FEBRUARY 10, 1943

HISTORY was repeating itself on the Russian front where another ex-corporal was retreating. Since this cartoon seems to tell its own story, there is nothing much left to say except that people often seem to wonder how a cartoonist's mind works. In this instance, given a blank sheet of paper, a deadline, the news of the day and some knowledge of history, the implications seem quite obvious.

What remains is working out the composition, such details as the skeletonized horse and something of the feeling of the vast Russian wastes over which Napoleon and Hitler had to retreat.

"THAT THESE DEAD SHALL NOT HAVE DIED IN VAIN"

FEBRUARY 12, 1943

THE time was arriving when thought could be given to peace and the hope of preserving it in the future. Lincoln's birthday offered an opportunity to combine these two themes.

90

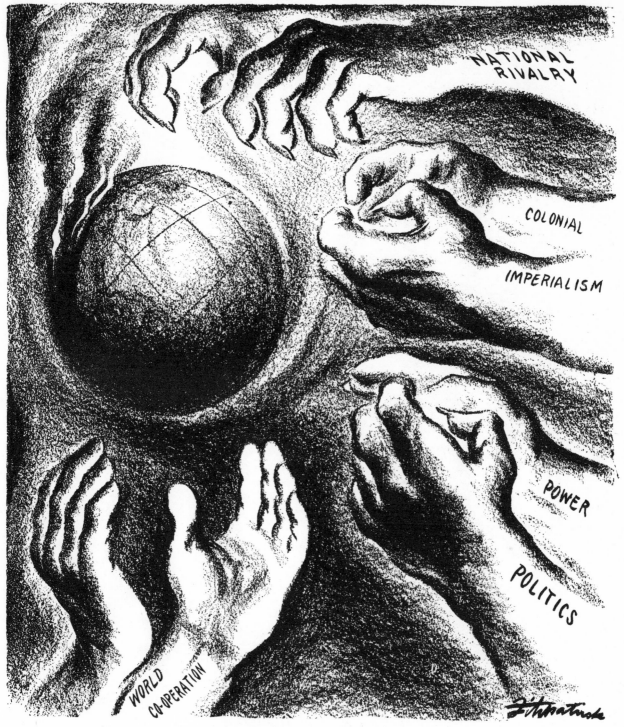

INTO WHOSE HANDS?
MARCH 10, 1943

THIS is another treatment of the coming postwar problems which seemed not too far in the offing in the light of the military situation.

In trying to distill this vast problem with its conflicting interests into a simple drawing, it was necessary to use several labels but I saw no way to avoid that and still make the meaning clear. The grasping hands should convey some message of warning as to what might happen in the future if these latent forces were to take over and wartime cooperation be forgotten.

91

1943 PARADE

SEPTEMBER 5, 1943

WOMANPOWER was the new order of the day. With women in the armed forces and thousands more in the factories, women became an important factor in the war picture.

92

EXIT
MAY 9, 1943

THE AXIS was at last driven out of Africa. General Rommel's Afrika Korps and his Italian allies had been crushed by the Anglo-American pincer under Generals Eisenhower and Montgomery. Meanwhile, American air power was reaching distant Berlin and the Nazi capital became the target of bombers which London had been earlier in the war. Death and destruction had returned to the nest where they were hatched.

"I'VE COME BACK HOME"
AUGUST 25, 1943

93

"HEIL!"
SEPTEMBER 7, 1943

EVENTS were catching up with the Nazi *Führer* and his gang. The famous *"Heil!"* salute is here translated into new and ominous pictorial terms. The New Year began with Hitler marching into total darkness with his now-tattered banner. The quotation from Mary Gardiner Brainard makes, I think, a very apt title for this cartoon.*

*From *Not Knowing*, stanza two

"I SEE NOT A STEP BEFORE ME AS I TREAD ON ANOTHER YEAR"
JANUARY 2, 1944

94

NEW NATIONAL ANTHEM
DECEMBER 20, 1943

THE ANTHEM of the selfish was being chanted by too many people at home while others on the war fronts were giving their lives for the common cause. Cartooning is not one of the precious arts and, in this instance, I had no hesitancy in using the methods of the comic page to indicate the song which was the main point of the cartoon.

AIR POWER had developed beyond the wildest dreams of only a few years earlier. Great forces now fought and maneuvered at high altitudes and one wondered what Lord Nelson would have thought of these new armadas of the air could he have looked up from his monument in Trafalgar Square. In contrast to the previous cartoon, this one is more of an illustration.

ARMIES IN THE SKY
JANUARY 14, 1944

"OYEZ, OYEZ, THE HONORABLE SUPREME COURT OF THE UNITED STATES—"
FEBRUARY 9, 1944

THE philosophy of the New Deal, which clashed with the opinions of the Supreme Court (see cartoon of May 19, 1936, on Page 20) and led to the defeated court-packing plan, still divided that tribunal.

Despite the fact that President Roosevelt had appointed a majority of the new justices, their differences continued to attract public attention and some of them appeared to be on a petty, personal basis.

NEW TIDE IN THE PACIFIC

FEBRUARY 10, 1944

THE early Japanese victories in the Pacific were petering out and a new pattern had formed. This is a fairly graphic example of pictorial expression. The Pacific theater suggested vast sea expanses. That was the first element to be considered from the visual language standpoint. Next, the power of the United States was becoming supreme in that area, so the problem was to combine these two facts into a picture. Drawing the flag so that it became a part of the surface of the wave may look easy in this reproduction, but working it out on the drawing board was a bit more difficult, and one thing a cartoonist likes to avoid is a tired, labored feeling in his finished drawing.

97

WHILE HITLER GUESSES

MAY 1, 1944

THE chief Axis partner in Europe faced the threat of invasion and the possibility, at long last, of a two-front war. General Eisenhower's forces in Britain were ready to strike.

IT COULDN'T BE DONE

JUNE 10, 1944

HITLER soon learned the impossible had happened and the unbreakable wall had been breached.

In this cartoon and the previous drawing of the fortress of Britain, the simple visual symbols, first of the fortress with its gangplank over the moat and second, the broken wall, im-mediately suggest to the reader the basic thought the cartoonist was trying to convey. The details are important but incidental to the main idea. The composition and execution are, or should be, elements for which the cartoonist has prepared himself by study, sketches from nature, and hard work.

99

UNITED FOR WAR, WHY NOT FOR PEACE?
JUNE 18, 1944

AGAIN the question of preparing for peace. Would the Allied powers, united in war, continue united in peace and build a stronger international organization than the League of Nations had proved to be after World War I, or would they fall apart into separate camps and leave the world to the grasping hands shown in the cartoon on Page 91.

100

G.O.P. DRAFT BOARD MEETS IN CHICAGO

JUNE 26, 1944

NEXT!

JULY 5, 1944

DESPITE the desperate battles of Europe and Asia, American democratic society conducted a national political campaign and elected a President. These three cartoons mark the highlights of that election. Governor Thomas E. Dewey of New York was the Republican candidate who ran against Franklin D. Roosevelt. For the benefit of the younger generation it might be necessary to explain that the long cigarette holder in the donkey's mouth in the cartoon of July 5, 1944, was a Roosevelt trademark.

NOW, BACK TO THE MAIN TASK

NOVEMBER 8, 1944

101

PHILIPPINE OPERATION
DECEMBER 18, 1944

BATAAN was avenged in the Pacific and the two-front squeeze was on in Europe. The once-potent Axis was on the way out. The invasion of the Philippines in 1944 climaxed the Allied campaign in the Pacific. Allied naval and air power had been rebuilt and attack operations had replaced defense. After a series of successful blows the Japanese had been dislodged from many key posts in the islands of the Central and Southwest Pacific while countless other islands had been by-passed and cut off.

THE BIG SQUEEZE IS ON
JANUARY 16, 1945

ON THE European front the Russians were fighting for two objectives, to drive the Germans from the soil of the Soviet Union and to completely distroy Hitler's army. Instead of retreating and saving his dwindling man-power, he decided to battle the now powerful Russian armies, with disastrous results.

The other side of the European pincer was General Eisenhower's armies, drawn up on the Reich frontier in preparation for another assault on the powerful Siegfried defense line.

UNTER DEN LINDEN
JANUARY 30, 1945

BERLIN, the capital of might, was a shambles because of Allied bombing. The conquerors of France who had marched on the Paris boulevards were home in a ghostly parade.

103

PRESIDENT ROOSEVELT died suddenly at Warm Springs, Georgia.

APRIL 13, 1945

STRENGTH TO YOUR ARM, MR. PRESIDENT
APRIL 15, 1945

VICE-PRESIDENT Truman took up the heavy burden.

THE ROOTS MUST COME UP
APRIL 17, 1945

WITH THE end of Hitler clearly in sight the next problem was to root out the Nazi spirit. I could think of no more simple, basic symbol than a tree and its roots with which everyone is familiar. Here again the Nazi swastika lent itself effectively to pictorial language.

WITNESSES FOR THE PROSECUTION
APRIL 30, 1945

JUDGMENT day was drawing near for the Nazi operators of gas chambers, bake ovens, and other forms of mass civilian murder. When the swift American armored units caught such places as Buchenwald unawares, unbelievable conditions were uncovered.

"DOWN TO BOTTOMLESS PERDITION"

MAY 7, 1945

GERMANY surrendered and the monstrous machine fell, into oblivion let us hope. Its chief engineer, Hitler, died a suicide in his Berlin bomb shelter.

LAST CHAPTER OF "MEIN KAMPF"
JUNE 8, 1945

PRESIDENT Roosevelt had warned the Nazi leaders (cartoon, October 16, 1942) that "Evidence is being relentlessly piled up." Now these butchers faced trial for their crimes.

A NEW ERA IN MAN'S UNDERSTANDING OF NATURE'S FORCES—President Truman

AUGUST 7, 1945

THE first atomic bomb fell on Hiroshima, Japan, and obliterated that city. A new force, not just another bomb, had been released. Whether it will be a servant or a master of mankind is still undecided.

111

OBSERVERS AT SAN FRANCISCO
APRIL 25, 1945

BUILDING the framework of peace began with the organization of the United Nations. The late Secretary of State, Edward Stettinius, requested the original of this cartoon which I sent to him. He must have gathered a number of United Nations cartoons because he also wrote me for some others I drew on the same subject. However, his collection could not have approached the number of originals President Truman gathered from various cartoonists. His collection was so large that I have often wondered whether it was a contributing factor in the threatened physical collapse of the White House.

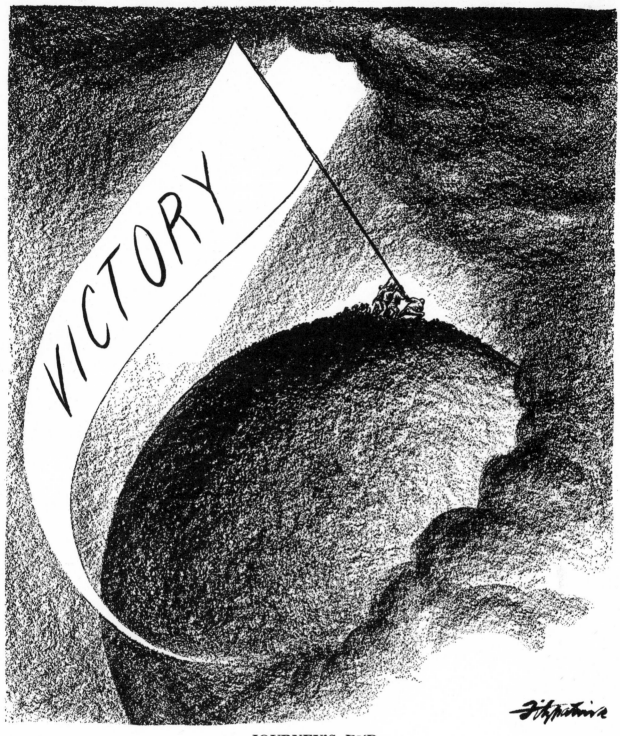

JOURNEY'S END
AUGUST 15, 1945

JAPAN surrendered and the long road of blood, sweat and tears officially ended. In this drawing the figures, while not too prominent, are in the same pose as in the famous photograph of our men raising the American flag on the peak of Iwo Jima.

113

THE atomic bomb was still with us. In a larger way the world found itself with a war souvenir far more potent than a live hand grenade. Unlike the hand grenade, atomic energy could be a force for good with its possibilities as a source of power, in the field of medicine, and probably in other uses. Whether man would use this new force for his benefit or for his destruction was and still is a subject for great debate.

WELL—?

OCTOBER 10, 1945

IN THE LABORATORY OF HUMAN AFFAIRS

OCTOBER 22, 1945

TO BE OR NOT TO BE

MAY 31, 1946

AMERICA'S PECULIAR GENIUS

AUGUST 27, 1946

"BE IT EVER SO HUMBLE"
NOVEMBER 9, 1945

WITH ALL of man's genius for invention and skill in war-making, he seemed unable to cope with the comparatively simple problem of housing. Poor housing in St. Louis had become a pressing national problem because of building restrictions, shortages in wartime, population growth and shifting of large groups to war industries in the cities.

This cartoon hardly exaggerates the situation.

116

DISPLACED PERSONS

AMONG THOSE PRESENT
NOVEMBER 25, 1945

PEACE became a displaced person while the victorious Allied powers struggled for a settlement. Russia's ambitions in Europe, especially in Germany, prevented any agreement.

117

"... SHALL NOT HAVE DIED IN VAIN"

NOVEMBER 27, 1945

DEBATE began in the United States Senate on our entry into the newly organized United Nations. With new weapons capable of reducing whole continents to rubble and remembering the countless lives already sacrificed in two world wars, a new peace was necessary. Such settlements as those of Versailles or the Congress of Vienna were not good enough this time.

118

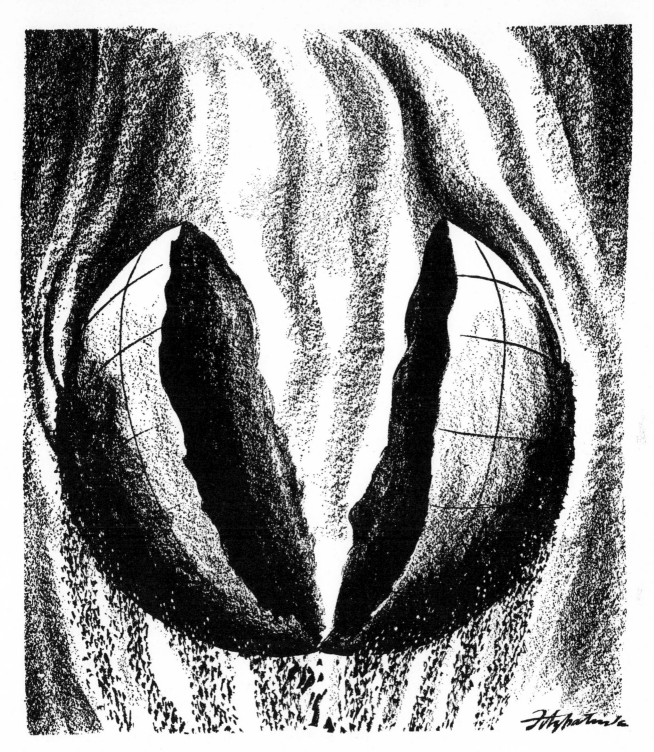

ONE WORLD OR TWO WORLDS?
MARCH 12, 1946

SOVIET Russia, with her new expanded frontiers and communist philosophy, dusted off the old Foreign Policy ambitions of the Czars and added touches of her own. As a result the world, despite all the talk of "one world," split in two.

LOST WEEKEND

FEBRUARY 11, 1946

FACING the difficult problems of the postwar world, the United States Senate was paralyzed by a minority group led by the late Senator Bilbo of Mississippi. Fair employment practices for all citizens met unfair political tactics and the filibusterers won the day.

120

WHAT OF OUR BIG COUNTRY?
MAY 24, 1946

IN AMERICA industrial war began, and one of the reasons for the struggle for higher wages was the hasty lifting of wartime control of prices with a resulting rise in living costs.

TEMPORARY PRICE CEILING

JULY 7, 1946

NOT THE MAN HE USED TO BE

SEPTEMBER 16, 1946

HE'S ALL YOURS

OCTOBER 21, 1946

CONGRESS had hacked price regulations of the Office of Price Administration to such an extent that most controls were lifted by November, 1946. Special interests, for whom the Senators had carved out loopholes in the law, saw an opportunity to turn a fast dollar. Unfortunately for everyone, the dollars they grabbed were victims of inflation which had been brought about, in part at least, by the very greed that demanded an end of controls.

END OF THE ROAD
SEPTEMBER 30, 1946

AT NUREMBERG, Germany, an international tribunal tried, sentenced, and executed the leaders of the Nazi murder gang. Here again is the swastika in another version.

123

No collection of *Post-Dispatch* cartoons would be complete without a few examples of the Rat Alley series. Rat Alley was an outgrowth of a series of "Thieves' Market" cartoons back in 1931 which were based on the looting of safe-deposit boxes of the Grand National Bank. A well-known St. Louis lawyer who was also a member of the Missouri Legislature acted as go-between in returning $822,000 of stolen, registered bonds for a $15,000 fee. The lawyer was never punished. The robbers were never convicted.

From the cartoon standpoint, "Rat Alley" is entirely different from the general run of my "distilled," simple compositions. It follows in a way my cartoon theory of change of pace and surprise punch that I had learned in boxing lessons years ago. Instead of using simple pictorial language, the alley is filled with signs and "balloons" common to the comic page. Rat Alley is a potent instrument and flexible enough to cover a variety of situations. One stock character, who never appears, speaks only from under the sewer cover.

An example of Rat Alley's realism was demonstrated to me when a cook at my home, who was from the deep South and had few friends in St. Louis, used to spend her time off riding all the street-car lines on a weekly pass. She really knew more about some parts of the city than I knew, but she surprised us one Monday morning by telling us she thought she had located Rat Alley on her week end jaunts and wanted us to confirm its location. I had sketched a lot of local streets and by-ways, so the details could have been found in any number of places in St. Louis.

On Sunday evening, February 17, 1952, the Reverend C. Oscar Johnson, pastor of one of the largest congregations in St. Louis, the Third Baptist, delivered a sermon entitled "Land of Shadows," based on the dark shadows and shadowy characters of Rat Alley. An original drawing of the Alley, published a few days earlier, was used to illustrate the sermon. A questionable local police board shake-up order and national scandals among public officials furnished the background for the sermon.

Rat Alley has become an institution in St. Louis.

RAT ALLEY CARRIES ON

AUGUST 7, 1943

RETREAT IN RAT ALLEY

NOVEMBER 6, 1943

NEW BUILDING IN RAT ALLEY

FEBRUARY 2, 1945

COMPETITION HITS EAST ST. LOUIS RAT ALLEY

SEPTEMBER 13, 1946

125

JOHN L. LEWIS'S SOUND EFFECTS
NOVEMBER 4, 1946

THE atomic bomb of American industrial war clicked on. With price controls weakened, wages naturally wanted to follow higher costs of living up the road. John L. Lewis demanded a corresponding increase for his coal miners—or else.

WEATHER CLEAR, TRACK FAST

DECEMBER 16, 1946

THE postwar race had started, but it looked as if the winners would eventually be paid with Chinese dollars.

127

"A MOUNTAIN TO SEE YOU, SIR"
FEBRUARY 23, 1947

Two centuries of British rule in India neared an end when Prime Minister Attlee announced definite withdrawal and set the date, June 1948. Mohandas K. Gandhi's long and unique campaign of "passive resistance" at last bore fruit. A London law graduate, Gandhi, after passage of the Rowlatt Acts (1919), organized a politico-religious movement of non-cooperation against the British Government of India.

Following the Mopla Rebellion (1921-22) and other riots, he was sentenced to prison for six years but released after two years because of serious illness. His methods of non-cooperation, "fast unto death," together with his recognized leadership of the Indian people, posed a problem no longer to be settled by force which was finally resolved by granting India independence.

128

TWILIGHT OF EMPIRE
MARCH 6, 1947

THE BRITISH, weakened by two world wars, were unable to maintain their old imperial position. Colonial peoples, for better or for worse, wanted to direct their own affairs. The British Commonwealth of Nations was replacing Queen Victoria's old Empire. New centers of world power were growing up in Washington and in Moscow. This cartoon and the one following definitely mark the end of one era and the beginning of another.

BURDENS OF EMPIRE
MARCH 16, 1947

PRESIDENT Truman's declaration of American policy in the Mediterranean recognized the vacuum created by British withdrawal from Greece and the reality of America's new position in the world—a reality which carried with it new and unaccustomed responsibilities.

GOING TO MEAN BELT TIGHTENING
MARCH 18, 1947

UNDER the old British Empire system, with its colonies scattered around the world, His Majesty's Navy automatically policed the seven seas and the remote places of the world. Now the United States had to take on some of that expensive task.

"HOW'M I DOING?"

MARCH 24, 1947

HASTY relaxing of price controls by Congress had not worked out as promised. The price bear was on his way up, and the lad who had him by the tail couldn't let go and couldn't hold him back.

132

TAFT—HARTLEY LAW

"SEEN ANYTHING OF JOHN LEWIS?"
JULY 17, 1947

REVISION of the Taft-Hartley Law was under discussion to clear up ambiguities and contradictions. One part, Section 304, known as the "political action" section, Senator Taft conceded might be ambiguous, but Representative Hartley disagreed.

The main idea seemed to be to stop Lewis, ambiguity or no ambiguity.

133

AN OLD BULB SPROUTING THIS SPRING
MARCH 23, 1947

THE federation of states idea had worked in America, Germany and the British dominions. Political rivalries and quarrels could be resolved by such a union of European states. Economic barriers could be removed, unified currency and other benefits might be derived from such an organization. Since the old balance-of-power formula had become so disrupted and individual European states were so weakened by war, it became imperative that they remember the old slogan of the American colonies, "Join or die."

LAST TIME HE SAW PARIS

JULY 2, 1947

AT A four-power meeting in Paris, Molotov rejected the aid offered under the Marshall Plan and Russia's satelites reluctantly had to follow suit. Santa Claus was not shot on this occasion, but he was certainly snubbed. The Russians then proceeded to try to wreck the plan.

THE KREMLIN PLAN

JULY 13, 1947

THE WAY BACK

JULY 20, 1947

WESTERN Europe was a defenseless wreck and an open invitation to invasion by the Soviet Union. In the interest of American security Secretary of State George C. Marshall, in a commencement address at Harvard, proposed reconstruction of Europe by a self-help plan assisted by the United States on a long-range basis. A three-power conference in Paris (June 27-July 2) was attended by Britain's Ernest Bevin, France's Georges Bidault, and Russia's Molotov. Molotov opposed the plan, but fourteen of twenty-two states invited to Paris on July 12 accepted it. They were Austria, Belgium, Denmark, Eire, Greece, Iceland, Italy, Luxemburg, Netherlands, Portugal, Sweden, Switzerland and Turkey.

Spain was not invited and the satellite countries followed Russia.

TWO WORLDS

JULY 24, 1947

THE United Nations Atomic Energy Commission made progress on an international control plan. The Commission voted ten to zero on December 30, 1946, for the plan, Russia and Poland not voting. This report went to the Security Council on the last day of 1946. Russia continued to fight against the plan and attack the good faith of the United States.

137

SAVING NICKELS IN THE DRY WAR

OCTOBER 14, 1947

CONGRESSIONAL economy prevented the Voice of America from competing with the powerful Voice of Moscow on anything like equal terms. American good will and peaceful intentions were supposed to be as well known abroad as they were at home, but unfortunately evidence was piling up rapidly that such was not the case.

ONE WORLD, IN FACT THE ONLY ONE
SEPTEMBER 8, 1947

AMERICAN economic problems were no longer simple neighborhood deals. Foreign trade and American dollars could affect the free world and a busted free world could affect us.

If we went hog-wild anything could happen.

NOT WHAT THEY SAID HE'D DO
SEPTEMBER 9, 1947

139

KANSAS CROP REPORT
SEPTEMBER 14, 1947

THIS early Kansas crop was blighted a few months later by a letter from the General to a Manchester (N.H.) publisher in January, 1948, which said: "In any event, my decision to remove myself completely from the political scene is definite and positive."

TOP PROBLEM
SEPTEMBER 16, 1947

THE decision by President Truman to step into the vacuum created by the decline of British power in the Mediterranean was one of major moves of his administration in its efforts to halt the forward march of communism.

OUR CARDS ON THE U.N. TABLE
SEPTEMBER 18, 1947

SPEAKING FOR THE U.S.S.R.
SEPTEMBER 21, 1947

141

PEACE-MONGERING

SEPTEMBER 23, 1947

THE Marshall Plan was another major effort by the Truman Administration in the Cold War. The Soviets called it "warmongering."

142

THE NEW BALANCE OF POWER
SEPTEMBER 26, 1947

FOOD was the great concern of the world in 1947, more than any other year in modern times. War shortages and slow recovery made for hunger, chaos and political revolt. For example only three million tons of rice were available to meet a minimum demand for eight million tons. President Truman sent ex-President Hoover to Europe as head of an economic mission. He reported the outlook very serious and called for vigorous United States action.

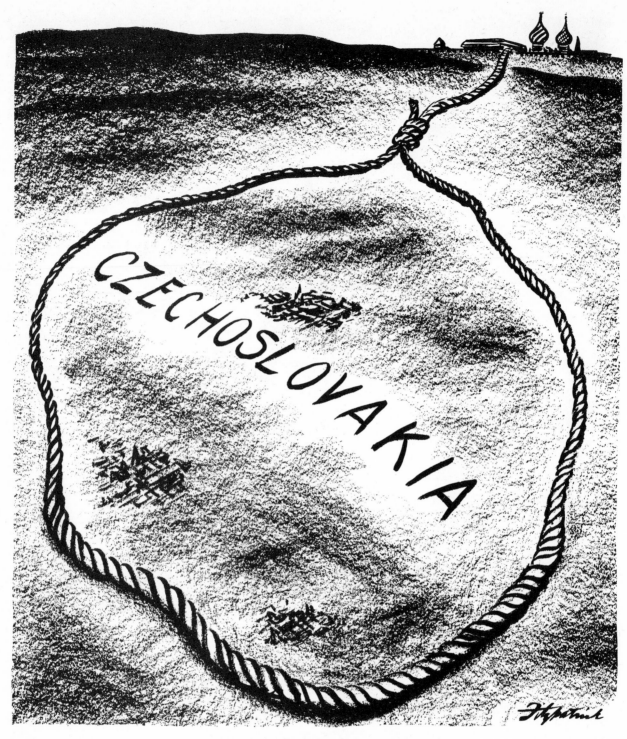

WHEN THE TIME IS RIPE—
NOVEMBER 10, 1947

THE independent republic of Czechoslovakia under President Beneš was ruled by a coalition government formed by four parties. Premier Gottwald's communist group was the strongest single party, and they endeavored to bring Czechoslovakia closer into line with Russian ideology, foreign policy, and commerce. Exploiting internal problems and national groups, the communists forced a crisis in Slovakia and demanded four representatives on non-parliamentary communist-controlled bodies to rule the regional administration.

The Kremlin noose was around Czechoslovakia.

IN SPECIAL SESSION IN EUROPE
NOVEMBER 16, 1947

Two grim figures watched over the destiny of Europe. Soviet Russia's technique of exploiting human misery and capitalizing on misfortune, until the victims were in her trap, stood to profit by winter cold and hunger in war-devastated Europe.

"HE DID IT!"
NOVEMBER 12, 1947

THE reactionary Republican Eightieth Congress had cut price controls and promised lower prices on the old "supply and demand" theory. They also figured the public would forget their actions by the time events caught up with them. Now we find each party accusing the other of knocking the bottom out of the consumer's market basket.

146

THINK FAST, BIG BOY!
DECEMBER 8, 1947

THE urgent need to control inflation and keep the American economy in balance in a troubled world brought no action from the Republican-controlled Congress. They finally packed up and went home for a Christmas vacation.

UNFINISHED BUSINESS
DECEMBER 19, 1947

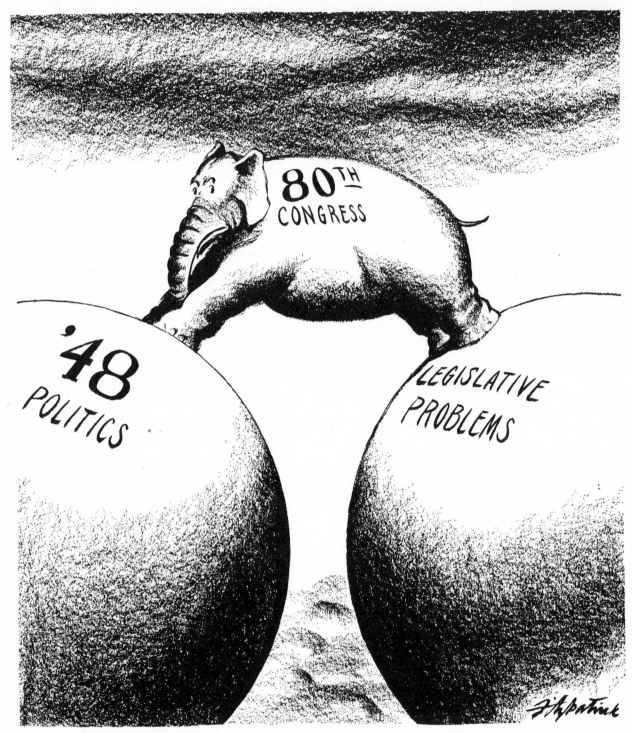

TWO WORLDS

JANUARY 4, 1948

THE year began with a Republican Congress divided between the coming national elections and the legislative needs of the nation. Inflation was the number-one problem, and the Marshall plan needed congressional action to aid Europe before the time ran out. Faced with these and other pressing domestic and international issues, would the party leaders face their responsibilities or pass the buck for votes in November?

THERE IS ALWAYS THIS POSSIBILITY

JANUARY 6, 1948

A SUB-COMMITTEE of the Senate Agriculture Committee investigating grain market speculators, who had been described by Secretary of Agriculture Anderson as "gamblers in human misery," dug up the name of Senator Elmer Thomas of Oklahoma, who admitted having traded on his own account in wheat, cotton and "possibly rye."

MORE THAN YOUR SLIP IS SHOWING, JOE
JANUARY 25, 1948

DETAILS of the earlier Nazi-Soviet pact were revealed by captured German documents.

The *Post-Dispatch* described them this way in an editorial: "The outlines of the plot could well have been conceived in the treacherous mind of Niccolo Machiavelli, and its execution entrusted to such a master of duplicity as Count de Talleyrand."

150

MARTYRS OF HUMANITY
FEBRUARY 12, 1948

MOHANDAS K. GANDHI, guiding spirit of the Indian independence movement, was murdered at a prayer meeting, January 30, 1948, by a Hindu party fanatic. His last years had been devoted to pacifying the violent quarrels which arose from the separation of Pakistan and India. His death was close enough to Lincoln's birthday and their spirits so kindred to each other that it seemed appropriate to combine them, if for no other reason than to help readers realize Gandhi's great contribution to his people and to history.

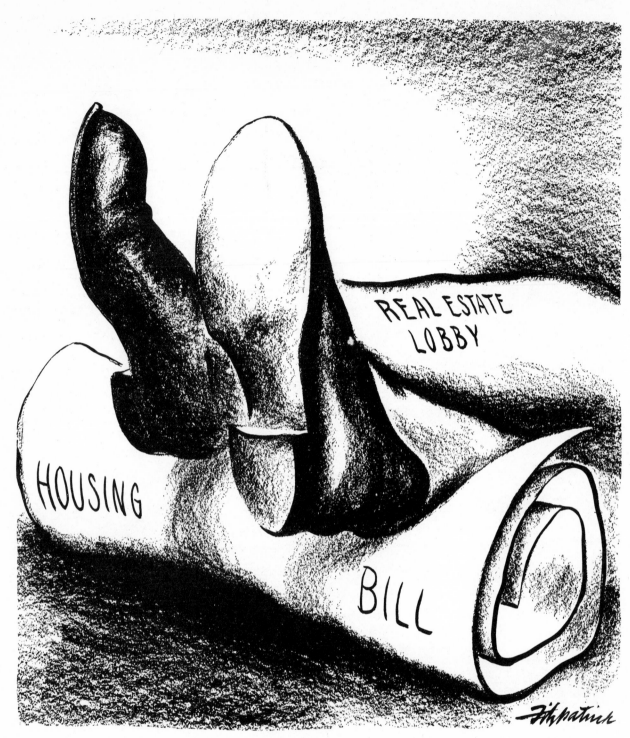

WHO'S WHO ON CAPITOL HILL
FEBRUARY 16, 1948

HOUSING was still a growing domestic issue and the powerful real estate lobby was playing footsie with members of Congress and with housing legislation.

152

THE NEW BIG BUSINESS
FEBRUARY 23, 1948

ORGANIZED crime had become a big business, national in scope, and with strong underground arteries. How wide its ramifications, the size of its financial operations, and its political influences was to be shown in detail in a later sensational Senate investigation.

**WORKERS OF CZECHOSLOVAKIA,
YOU HAVE NOTHING TO GAIN BUT YOUR CHAINS**
FEBRUARY 24, 1948

THE independent republic of Czechoslovakia became a "people's democracy," Soviet style, in February, 1948. The crisis came about over who was to control the police in the coming elections. With a communist Premier and a communist Interior Secretary, that question was easily answered. Armed communist "action committees" did the rough stuff. President Beneš tried to hold the old National front, but to no avail. A new government was formed in which communists held all key posts.

MANY subjects repeat themselves year after year. Easter is one of them, and the cartoonist wonders what new treatment he can give this ancient event. Easter Sunday shouldn't be a grim day. Readers are in no mood for heavy editorial thunder, and yet the cartoonist, while recognizing the anniversary, must also recognize the facts we are living with. At a quick glance the Easter lilies dominate this cartoon, but one of the leaves in the bouquet is obviously too hardy to bend over.

EASTER BOUQUET—1948
MARCH 28, 1948

154

WAITING FOR THE WINDFALL
FEBRUARY 25, 1948

HENRY WALLACE, who missed the Presidency by being Vice-President in the wrong Roosevelt administration, had left the Truman cabinet where he had been Secretary of Commerce. With Truman coming up for election on his own, Wallace bolted the party and organized a third party which took the name of the old La Follette "Progressive" party. This new organization had no connection whatever with the La Follettes'.

ELEVENTH HOUR
MARCH 9, 1948

TIME WAS running out on rehabilitating Europe and halting the communist gains. But the Eightieth Congress had political fish to fry in a year of national elections, and implementing the Marshall plan was not on that menu.

NOT A STRIKE, JUST MENTAL TELEPATHY

MARCH 16, 1948

LAWS which prevented union officials from calling strikes could not be applied to walkouts which occurred spontaneously, as it were.

ALL THIS AND BRICKBATS TOO?

MARCH 26, 1948

THE President had his hands full, 1948 being an election year.

BRICKBATS were being tossed at the Administration, but the opposition was catching something more useful.

THEM THAT HATH

JUNE 20, 1948

VOICE OF ITALY
APRIL 21, 1948

THE republic of Italy's first general election to both the Chamber of Deputies and the Senate became a clear struggle between the Catholic Church and the communist *Fronte Democratico Popolare.*

The contest also became an international test between East and West. The governments of the United States, Britain and France announced they wished to offer a new clause in the peace treaty granting Trieste to Italy. This move handicapped the left *Fronte* campaigners, and despite a violent pre-election campaign the voting was peaceful and the communists took a beating.

HOW TO CLOSE THE GAP?
JUNE 7, 1948

BERLIN was divided into two opposing sectors in June, 1948, after the breakdown of the four-power control. The Soviet then attempted to drive the Western powers from the city by every possible means short of an outright act of war. Searches and inspections of trucks, trains and river barges were instigated merely for delay and blockade purposes. Russian fighter planes held maneuvers near civil airports to impede recognized air-traffic lanes. Marshall Sokolovski proclaimed to the Berliners that the Western powers had no longer any right to remain in the city since the four-power *Kommandatura* no longer existed.

THE RED SEA CLOSES OVER CZECHOSLOVAKIA
JUNE 8, 1948

PRESIDENT BENEŠ resigned on June 7 and, although in bad health, he made it clear his motives were political, not personal. On March 10, Jan Masaryk, foreign minister since 1941 and last male member of the family of the famed president-liberator, was found dead outside the window of his apartment in the Ministry. These events and a series of purges ended the fiction of a free Czechoslovakia. The iron curtain had been rung down.

UNEASY PATH
JUNE 30, 1948

SATELLITE communist officials learned that independent parties were a myth—many of them learned it the hard way. The Yugoslav communists, under the leadership of Marshal Tito, were publicly called to task for not obeying directives from the Moscow Politburo and Marshal Stalin. In the world of international communism Moscow leadership became infallible.

160

"INFIDEL!"

JULY 11, 1948

MARSHAL TITO refused to knuckle under. He was denounced for following "an incorrect line on the basic questions of foreign and domestic policy" and carrying out "a hateful policy in relation to the U.S.S.R." Tito's reply in a letter to Stalin was: "... even though we love the U.S.S.R. we cannot love our own country less." Yugoslavia became a "diversionist bandit" in Red circles.

THE UNDERGROUND WAR

SEPTEMBER 2, 1948

THE Master of Moscow was having troubles of his own.

IN THE CAPITAL OF ILLINOIS
SEPTEMBER 9, 1948

THE GREEN MACHINE INVESTIGATES ITSELF
SEPTEMBER 15, 1948

THE GREEN MACHINE PREPARES ITS BATH
SEPTEMBER 19, 1948

THE *Post-Dispatch* conducted a major campaign against the Green Machine in Illinois in the 1948 elections. We are just across the river from Illinois, and East St. Louis is actually part of our population area.

What happens in southern Illinois, whether it is a coal mine disaster, gang wars, or gambling rackets tied in with corrupt office-holders, is, we feel, part of our community concern.

Adlai E. Stevenson was elected governor to succeed Green.

THE SHOW MUST GO ON

JULY 13, 1948

THE NEXT SPEAKER—

OCTOBER 31, 1948

The Democratic National Convention of 1948 opened in Philadelphia in an atmosphere of gloom. The Republicans and their candidate, Governor Dewey, were full of confidence. All the democrats were discouraged—all but President Truman, who took to the road on a "whistle stop" speech-making campaign. When the votes were counted, there was a great awakening in both camps and among the "political expert forecasters."

SAID SOMETHING!

NOVEMBER 3, 1948

AT THE HOW-DID-IT-HAPPEN CLUB

NOVEMBER 7, 1948

163

OUR PART OF THE WORLD

OCTOBER 28, 1948

THE North Atlantic Alliance, consisting of Great Britain, France, Belgium, the Netherlands, Luxemburg and the United States, was, as its name implies, a grouping of North Atlantic nations for the purpose of pooling their defense resources.

Rearmament was brought about because the Soviet Union had failed to demobilize its forces following World War II as had the other major powers. Regional defense pacts were formed within the framework of the United Nations.

ROAD TO RUIN
NOVEMBER 12, 1948

CHINESE Nationalist forces had gradually lost their superiority in manpower and equipment through corrupt administration, uninspired leadership and defections in its forces. They also lost the initiative to the increasingly powerful communist armies. Mukden fell on October 30 and with it went all of Manchuria. Other key points surrendered to the Reds until the Yangtze became the Nationalists' last line of defense against attacks on Nanking and Shanghai. The communists proclaimed a North China People's Government and published a list of "war criminals" headed by Chiang Kai-shek.

A settlement between the warring Chinese factions now seemed out of the question.

O SAY, CAN'T YOU SEE?
NOVEMBER 17, 1948

WHILE the government of old China lay dying, a new state was being born in Palestine. A resolution of the General Assembly of the United Nations had recommended in 1947 the partition of Palestine into two independent states—Arab and Jewish—with Jerusalem and the surrounding territory to be internation-alized. The Jewish National Council in Pales-tine, at the termination of the British Mandate, proclaimed on May 14, 1948, the establishment of the new Jewish state to be called Israel. Its admission to United Nations membership was postponed until peace and more definite fron-tiers had been established.

BACK TO THE OLD PATTERN?
NOVEMBER 23, 1948

THE huge Ruhr heavy industries were the backbone of Hitler's power and their control was of vital importance. The United States intervened to modify British and French policies. British and United States Military Governors announced a new interim plan covering control of six steel companies, fourteen coal firms and four electrical concerns. France objected to the plan because it feared the interim arrangement, to which it took exception, would in its nature become permanent.

Again we have the swastika symbol in a new setting. The visual impact of the Nazi emblem is the first thing to meet the reader's eye, and it carries an instant message. Here we have the problem of the industrial heart of Western Europe, its possible future, shape and control. So it seems natural to use factories to suggest industry and shape the factories into the symbol they might become again if they fell into wrong hands as a single unit. All this is conveyed at a glance and it is my practice, whenever possible, to portray the basic thing the drawing is about. For example, if it be a coal strike, coal or something akin to the coal industry should let the reader know at first glance what the subject is about without having to read too many labels.

CREATED
BY
SOVIET SCIENTIST
IVAN POPOFF

DESIGNED
BY
SOVIET SCIENTIST
STARDUSTOVSKY

INVENTED
BY
SOVIET SCIENTIST
MOONSHINEOVITCH

AND ON THE SEVENTH DAY STALIN RESTED
JANUARY 12, 1949

SOVIET propaganda was reconditioning the minds of the Russian people.

One of its side-lines was claiming every invention known to mankind as the creation of some Russian genius who was obviously inspired by the great Stalin, even if the alleged inventor had lived back in the days of Ivan the Terrible.

MAN'S BRIGHT FUTURE OR HIS LAST MILE?
FEBRUARY 6, 1949

THE DOOR was opening on a new era for mankind if only— The hitch was whether atomic energy would be used for constructive or destructive purposes. So great was its potential that the shape of things could be changed whichever way it went. In countries like England, with depleted coal reserves and no hydroelectric power sources, atomic power could mean as important an opportunity as did the steam engine in its day.

SABOTAGING DEMOCRACY
MARCH 16, 1949

IMPORTANT legislation awaited action in the "world's greatest deliberative body" while the Senators—again the Republican-Southern Democrat combination—frittered away time with a filibuster. On this occasion the tactic was first used to stop a movement to change the rules which would make it possible to break a filibuster and later to change the rules so as to make it impossible to stop one.

169

BANNER OF THE NON-SOVIET UNION
MARCH 18, 1949

FROM behind his iron barrier the Russian gazed across a Europe united under a banner of unity which would not have been possible without the Russian's own threat. Fear of Soviet aggression caused ancient differences to be set aside.

Mere survival now meant more than national pride and rivalry.

170

THE MEETING WILL NOW COME TO ORDER
APRIL 7, 1949

DESPITE the great divide which separated the Soviet Union and the Western powers, the four-year-old United Nations was still a meeting ground for discussion. Control of atomic energy and reduction of armaments remained major differences, but the United Nations— because of its flexibility and methods—was able to achieve important results in social, political and economic fields through its special agencies.

The bridge was still there even if the gap was wide.

"PEACE HATH ITS VICTORIES—"

APRIL 28, 1949

THE Russian rail, highway and waterway blockade of Berlin to force the Western powers out of the city failed when the air lift, known as "Operation Vittles," succeeded in supplying the city with its needs, even to hauling in coal and operating in all kinds of weather. The air lift began in June, 1948, and during its fifteen months of operations, United States planes carried in 1,783,826 tons and British planes carried 538,416 tons.

Even the Russians, who have a high regard for Western mechanical and scientific genius, must have secretly admired "Operation Vittles."

OUR THREE-PARTY SYSTEM IN CONGRESS

MAY 23, 1949

PRESIDENT Truman's victory at the polls and his introduction of his Fair Deal program failed to get the support in Congress the voters had given him in the election. If the Roosevelt New Deal had been anathema in certain sectors, the Truman Fair Deal was worse. The result in Congress was, in effect, a three-party system consisting of Truman Democrats, regular Republicans, and a combination of conversative Democrats and Old Guard Republicans.

173

WEIGHING HIS CHANCES

MAY 26, 1949

THE Master of the Kremlin controlled a vast empire stretching from the borders of Western Europe to the Pacific, but his ambitions were not limited, even with such a wide horizon. The industrial potential of Western Europe and the mass of land and manpower in Asia were both tempting opportunities. The question seemed to be, which one was the bargain?

174

THE TAIL THAT WANTS TO WAG THE DOG
JUNE 1, 1949

THE East German constitution had been put together almost overnight by a "people's congress."

Its purpose was to offset the West German-Bonn constitution and also for Vishinsky's use in debate at the meeting of Foreign Ministers in Paris, where he made use of the dog's tail.

175

DEBATE ON THE TAFT-HARTLEY ACT
JUNE 10, 1949

FRUSTRATION, resulting from the maneuvers of John L. Lewis and his coal miners, caused the Congress to aim labor legislation at one target.

"I CAN GIVE THEE BUT A SONG"
JUNE 24, 1949

THE Missouri do-nothing legislature came through with an enactment which might be called "cultural" legislation when it made the "Missouri Waltz" the official state song.

ON THE JUST AND ON THE UNJUST
JUNE 12, 1949

COMMUNIST aggression throughout the world, plus the sensational activities of the House Un-American Activities Committee over a period of years eventually resulted in a state of national jitters. Any political demagogue could make headlines by accusing anyone of being a communist or a fellow-traveler. The just and the unjust alike were smeared, and generally the smear stuck regardless of its justice or its injustice.

A-BOMB RUINS IN AMERICA
SEPTEMBER 28, 1949

178

CONSTITUTION
OF THE
UNITED STATES

PROMOTE THE GENERAL WELFARE

IN CASE ANY VISITORS LEFT THEIR GLASSES AT HOME
SEPTEMBER 7, 1949

THE American Bar Association was meeting in St. Louis. Eleven years earlier the Association had appointed a distinguished committee to assist in protecting civil rights. The high quality of their work was carried on up to the time of the present committee, which seemed to regard the welfare of the citizenery as a whole rather than the individual's welfare as its particular responsibility. A year previously the committee had gone to the aid of the House Un-American Activities Committee, and it also had recommended the Mundt-Nixon bill, which would have done more harm than good in controlling subversive influences.

"O TITO, YOO HOO!"
AUGUST 24, 1949

THE USUAL Kremlin tactics weren't working
out in Yugoslavia.

THE DIVISION of Germany into two separate
states became a fact with the establishment
of the East German democratic republic and
the West German federal republic in 1949.
Extensive powers were granted to the West
German republic with important exceptions,
including demilitarization, disarmament,
Ruhr control, and various trade restrictions.
The occupying powers still reserved the right
to resume full control in an emergency, but
this was the first major step toward the resto-
ration of the German state. And it was hoped
the new Germany would not walk in the same
path that lead to 1918 and to 1945.

LEST THEY FORGET
SEPTEMBER 15, 1949

180

"MORE AMERICANS TO SEE YOU, EL CAUDILLO"
SEPTEMBER 27, 1949

THE SPANISH dictator had few friends in Europe after the fall of Hitler and Mussolini, but he seemed to be becoming popular in some American circles.

THE CORRUPT Nationalist leaders of China were getting out with their private fortunes and leaving behind a trail their incompetence helped create.

THE TRAIL HE LEFT BEHIND HIM
SEPTEMBER 29, 1949

181

TOUGH CHOICE
OCTOBER 3, 1949

THE Republican elephant paused to consider his future plans. Recent platforms and candidates did not differ greatly with the opposition and had been criticized within the party as "me too" candidates. In other words they were practically for the New Deal, but promised to administer it better. This was not enough to form a real opposition and the question was—what other stand would attract a following at the polls?

...THIS GIANT SPECTER OF HUMAN DERELICTION...

OCTOBER 4, 1949

DISPLACED persons who had been driven from their homelands during and after the war were a tragic by-product of that struggle. The International Refugee Organization, a specialized agency of the United Nations, took on the problem, and 318,096 D.P.'s were resettled from Germany, Austria and Italy during 1949. By January, 1950, less than 40,000 refugees remained in central Europe. But enough people of all groups were crowded in the European camps to arouse the conscience of the free world.

LATEST PICKET LINE
OCTOBER 7, 1949

UNIFICATION of the armed forces under one cabinet officer, the Secretary of Defense, was meeting strong Naval opposition. There was something about drawing an admiral on a picket line which struck me as one way of making high brass realize the meaning of its actions. And, since mutiny is a big word in Naval and maritime circles, I worked it into the other cartoon.

In cartooning, as in other types of warfare, different weapons are used. If a flit gun serves the purpose, why waste a torpedo? This seemed a minor action and not a task-force job.

"WHAT SAY, ADMIRAL?"
OCTOBER 16, 1949

IMPLEMENTING THE "PEOPLE'S REPUBLIC"
OCTOBER 26, 1949

COMMUNIST-RULED Czechoslovakia was feeling the weight of the new regime. The Czech Catholic Church had felt the heavy hand, and a series of conspiracy trials resulted in the execution of General Heliodor Pika and the life imprisonment of General Karel Kutlvasr. Six other persons were executed for plotting and ten sentenced to life. Thousands of communist party members were expelled. The power from over the horizon was asserting its authority in the usual way.

RUSSIAN expansion was advancing while colonialism was becoming a thing of the past in the rest of the world. The absentee landlordism practiced by various European powers over the backward countries of the world was being liquidated. Self-determination advanced by Woodrow Wilson following World War I had seeped into the far corners of the earth. In Asia the Japanese slogan, "Asia for the Asiatics," had a powerful influence, especially so after the quick, easy victories of the Japanese in the early days of the war in the Pacific. For a long time I had had in the back of my head that quotation,

He was a leader of that forlorn orchestra
To whose piping no one dances . . .
and here was a chance to use it.

"TO WHOSE PIPING NO ONE DANCES"
NOVEMBER 4, 1949

185

NEW PAGE IN A LONG HISTORY
DECEMBER 9, 1949

On December 8, 1949, the Nationalist capital was moved to Taipei, Formosa, and the People's Government controlled the mainland of China and declared itself the legal government of China. The U.S.S.R. announced diplomatic recognition and all other communist-controlled countries followed suit. Burma and India extended *de jure* (legal) recognition. Britain offered *de jure* recognition but no formal diplomatic relations had been established. On January 10, 1950, the Red government expressed willingness to negotiate to open diplomatic relations. Tough bargaining lay ahead on old treaties and agreements, particularly the status of Hong Kong.

Old China was beginning a new diary.

"AND THIS IS THE MISSUS"
DECEMBER 14, 1949

186

LACK of cooperation between the Soviet Union and the Western powers continued to plague the world, and this cartoon raised the question of whether an understanding could be reached over an obviously long and difficult trail.

AN IMPOSSIBLE TRAIL?
FEBRUARY 22, 1950

AMERICA'S new role in world affairs put new burdens on our State Department at a time when international relations were in a difficult and explosive condition. Senator Mc-Carthy, under the protection of congressional immunity, added to that burden by smearing the department with wild, unfounded charges of disloyalty. This cartoon was published without a title.

MARCH 21, 1950

187

MEETING OF THE BOARD OF DIRECTORS
APRIL 14, 1950

THE big business of Crime, Incorporated, was attracting attention. The huge revenues from commercial gambling financed the operations, which could not function without the acquiescence of law-enforcement officials. This meant a tie-up of crime and politics which was to be exposed later in detail by a committee of the United States Senate.

OUR INDUSTRIAL PANMUNJOM

MAY 1, 1952

No PROGRESS was being made toward a settlement of the steel strike.

"PEACE" MOVEMENT IN KOREA
JUNE 27, 1950

SHORTLY before the end of World War II the Soviet Union declared war on Japan in order to participate in the Pacific victory. For military purposes the thirty-eighth parallel in Korea was designated as a dividing line. Later United Nations resolutions called for a national election, under observation of a United Nations Commission, for the purpose of electing an assembly and establishing a national government. This did not fit into Soviet plans, and when the Republic of Korea was inaugurated in 1948, north of the thirty-eighth parallel the Soviets established a People's Democratic Republic of Korea. Raids were soon conducted across the border. Without warning, on June 25, 1950, at 4 A.M., North Korean forces struck. This formidable attack was implemented with Soviet tanks and other equipment. Russian peace propaganda wore a new face in Korea.

JULY 6, 1950

WOULD World War III be touched off in Korea? Had Stalin selected this theater for one of his stooges to drag United States military resources into the bog of Asia? Were we to abandon Western Europe and gamble our chips in the Orient? Behind the North Korean puppet, Stalin seemed to be saying to the United States and Red China, "Let's you and him fight." This cartoon was published without a title.

191

GRAB THOSE REINS, UNCLE!
JULY 25, 1950

THE SINS of the "Eighty-worst" Congress and prematurely relaxed price-wage controls were catching up with us. The run-away nag was on his way with no hands on the reins.

HORNS OF THE DILEMMA
SEPTEMBER 12, 1950

WOULD a rearmed Germany revert to Nazi ambitions or throw its powerful weight to the Soviet side as Hitler had done in his prewar treaty with the Kremlin? These were vital questions for the occupying Western powers in the international poker game.

192

THE THREAT
NOVEMBER 7, 1950

THE Soviet stooge system was working well in Korea. Red China forces moved in, of course on a purely "volunteer" basis, to help the puppet state of North Korea. Stalin could still talk peace through his propaganda megaphone while his satellite agents could make war "unofficially" and be assured of Soviet guns, planes and tanks. The "volunteer, unofficial" action of Red China kept her from setting the world afire but it still left the world in a shaky position.

TOTTERING
NOVEMBER 26, 1950

193

THE TIME IS NOW
DECEMBER 17, 1950

MEANWHILE, the United States, which had demobilized its forces too quickly following victory in World War II, began to rebuild its stack of chips for the international poker game.

194

THE SOVIET PLAN
JANUARY 11, 1951

VISHINSKY made a play for German sympathy by advocating a unified Reich. The catch was that smaller East Germany had been rearmed by the Reds under the guise of a "police force." Under this unification plan the "police force" would be expected, in any unification, to take over unarmed West Germany and rule the roost.

195

CROOKED OR JUST FUNNY LOOKING?

FEBRUARY 22, 1951

SENATOR Fulbright, chairman of the Senate Banking Subcommittee, after a year of investigating the Reconstruction Finance Corporation, issued a report which charged mismanagement and urged reorganization by replacing the RFC board of directors with a single administrator who would have full responsibility for the job.

EAST SIDE, WEST SIDE, ALL AROUND RAT ALLEY
FEBRUARY 23, 1951

SENATOR Kefauver's crime investigation held one of its sessions in St. Louis. The ramifications of organized rackets and their political alliances extended from one end of the country to the other. Commercialized gambling was the big money-maker, with dope peddling and other activities as sidelines. Politics entered the picture because the gangs couldn't operate without the protection of law-enforcement officers. Rat Alley became a national thoroughfare on this occasion and a newcomer, television, paraded before the public some of the most fantastic characters and testimony. This real-life drama—something everyone could understand—was, indeed, stranger than fiction.

NEWCOMER IN RAT ALLEY
MARCH 22, 1951

197

HOW THE PUTSCH TOOK MARYLAND
MARCH 18, 1951

SENATOR Tydings of Maryland, one of the ultra-conservative Democrats, was defeated for re-election in a smear campaign organized outside the Free State. Earlier the Senator had headed a committee which investigated Senator McCarthy's charges against the State Department, and his committee report officially branded the charges a fraud. For this report he was purged at the polls. A new, sinister technique was introduced into the American system of elections, and Senator Tydings was one of its first victims.

IN THE UN-FREE WORLD OF ARGENTINA

APRIL 3, 1951

THE South American dictator, Peron, was following the pattern of his European prototypes. Free press, free speech, and political opposition to the regime were ruthlessly suppressed. Like all dictators he blamed any shortcomings at home on outside enemies; in this instance United States imperialism was his whipping boy.

199

NOT A GENERAL'S JOB
APRIL 10, 1951

THE cartoon of April 10, 1951, appeared the day before the President's removal of General MacArthur from his Pacific command post. This drawing and the two following cartoons make it clear that, in our opinion, the General—who was also United Nations commander of the armies fighting in Korea—was exceeding his authority and attempting to usurp the powers of his policy-making superiors by extending the war beyond the confines of Korea, with all the possibilities such action might entail.

WE ARE STILL UNDER CIVILIAN RULE
APRIL 12, 1951

WHAT WELCOME IN AMERICA FOR ME?
APRIL 18, 1951

WAGING PEACE IN KOREA

APRIL 26, 1951

CONSISTENCY played no part in communist propaganda. Their words and actions could be completely contradictory as they are shown here. Peace was their great ballyhoo at the same time they were arming and directing their stooges warring in Korea.

IF OUR LAWMAKERS FAIL US
JUNE 17, 1951

CONTINUING subjects, such as inflation, involve discovering new ways of presenting what is essentially the same idea. Fortunately this subject had many aspects which could be explored, and by showing all phases of inflation's prog-ress the people could be given a better understanding of the problem. It was hoped that they might also remember what leaders of Congress did in 1947 when they ended price control.

"YOU'RE SURE IT'LL ALL BE ON THE UP-AND-UP, SENATOR?"

JUNE 25, 1951

SENATOR McCarthy's political tactics, demonstrated in the Maryland campaign against Senator Tydings, and his venomous attacks on General Marshall made some of the more respectable Republican leaders skeptical of his support of "Mr. Republican," Senator Taft, for President.

But votes were votes and, if Senator McCarthy could deliver them, his methods might be overlooked.

203

AS THE WATERS RECEDE
AUGUST 16, 1951

MISSOURI River floods again collected a fearful toll. Kansas City especially suffered heavy losses. And on the great farming lands along the river in the heart of America's bread-basket, the devastation ran into hundreds of millions of dollars. Unified planning and control of the Missouri Valley, a plan similar to TVA, which was a demonstrated success in the Tennessee Valley, would seem to be the obvious answer to this problem. But powerful interests, headed by the Corps of Army Engineers, insisted on following the old divided authority and spot-control system, and opposed all efforts at regional control.

HOW'S FOR A NEW GOAL?
SEPTEMBER 12, 1951

THE big business of college football attracted the big gambling fraternity. These professionals were looking for "sure-thing" bets, and the way to get them was to fix the games by bribing the players. Scandals resulted in focusing attention on the question of whether colleges were primarily educational institutions or merely home grounds for football teams.

WASHINGTON scandals were headline news. Senator Fulbright's investigation of the RFC disclosed five per cent influence peddlers— fixers who gave Government officials everything from hams to mink coats for their wives. The Bureau of Internal Revenue and the Department of Justice came under scrutiny of House subcommittee of the Ways and Means Committee, headed by Congressman King, Democrat, of California.

The RFC Lithofold loan case was unearthed by the *Post-Dispatch* in its investigation of St. Louis Internal Revenue Collector James P. Finnegan. The loan had been rejected several times until the right person applied; then it got very prompt action. As the probe continued it became apparent that the scandals in the Internal Revenue Department were on a national scale. Brooklyn, Boston, San Francisco and St. Louis seemed to follow the same pattern. They also had in common politically appointed Collectors who considered their posts part-time jobs, and, if they were lawyers, they continued to practice their profession on the side. Big and little tax dodgers were, naturally, interested in the services of an attorney who was also a tax official with wide discretionary powers.

President Truman has since proposed to Congress that Collectors be taken out of the system of political patronage and put under Civil Service.

News of these cheap deals and petty rackets were broadcast to the world over news wires, and the effect on foreigners we were trying to convince of our high purposes in crusading against communism can only be guessed at.

EXPORTS IN AMERICA'S "POINT FIVE" PROGRAM
DECEMBER 9, 1951

WHO'S WHO AND WHAT'S WHAT
SEPTEMBER 21, 1951

FROM ALL DIRECTIONS
OCTOBER 30, 1951

"I THINK I NEED A GOOD LAWYER"
OCTOBER 5, 1951

PLAYING TOO MANY PARTS
OCTOBER 12, 1951

Iran, Egypt and the Near East were all in a turmoil as the British faced general elections. Fanatical demagogues in Egypt, for example, had been covering up their own exploitation of the masses by blaming poverty and misery on the "foreign devil." Earlier British colonial exploitation may have been a contributing factor, but land reform and other changes by their own leaders could have improved the lot of the people.

GOOD ACT IF—

OCTOBER 11, 1951

DANGEROUS DETOUR

OCTOBER 24, 1951

HEART OF THE STORM

NOVEMBER 6, 1951

208

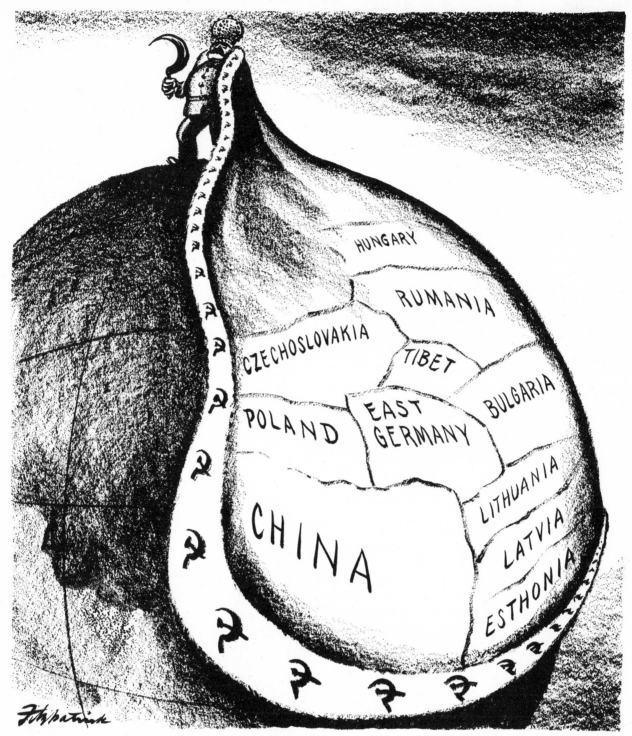

THE NEW IMPERIALISM
OCTOBER 28, 1951

As THE old colonial empires of the Western European powers disintegrated, a new imperialism arose. Its terminology and propaganda slogans did not alter the fact that the "people's republics" were ruled from Moscow. Stalin dictated with an efficiency the old Czars would have envied, and he had an expansion program beyond the dreams of the Romanoffs.

209

THE Ellen Knauff case was especially inspiring to me because it demonstrated the workings of our free system and free press at its best. Ellen Knauff was an unknown war bride about to be excluded from citizenship; Irving Dilliard, editorial page editor of the *Post-Dispatch*, noted a brief paragraph about her buried in a wire news story. Despite the distorted idea many people seem to have as to what motivates the press, Ellen Knauff was not a big advertiser, she was not even a subscriber; in fact, she didn't know of this newspaper's existence when she was confined to Ellis Island. But Editor Dilliard believed her case involved simple justice because refusal to admit her was an arbitrary action by a bureaucrat in the name of "national security."

A campaign for a fair hearing was begun January 18, 1950, and in the course of that fight eleven cartoons appeared on this one subject. For months the newspaper stood almost alone. Before the hearing ended, Congress, the Supreme Court and Department of Justice heard of Ellen Knauff. Representative Francis E. Walter of Pennsylvania, Senator Lehman and Representative Roosevelt of New York were recruited on her side and worked effectively in her behalf. Eventually it became front-page news over the country. The case ended when Attorney General McGrath admitted her to citizenship under the law as the war bride of a combat GI.

The Attorney General's reversal was a courageous move because it repudiated the original action of former Attorney General Clark, then a member of the Supreme Court, as well as overruling the actions of various subordinates under his own jurisdiction.

UNTO THE LEAST OF THESE
NOVEMBER 4, 1951

THE NIGHT VISHINSKY COULDN'T SLEEP FOR LAUGHING
NOVEMBER 16, 1951

VISHINSKY's tirade in reply to Secretary of State Acheson's disarmament plan, including atomic control, before the United Nations Security Council in Paris included this gem:

I could hardly sleep all night last night after having read that speech. I could not sleep because I kept laughing. Usually I do not go around laughing but really, even from this rostrum—

although I am trying to keep within the bounds of decorum out of consideration for you, Mr. President, I cannot restrain my laughter in connection with this so-called peace proposal by which the United States of America have tried to wrest initiative from the Soviet Union.

Rumor had it that Vishinsky's laughter sounded a sour note even in Moscow, and he hasn't even giggled in recent news reports.

211

NO BETTER ALTAR?
DECEMBER 26, 1951

ALMOST on Christmas Eve Orient Mine #2 at West Frankfort, Illinois, exploded and left one hundred and seventy-six orphans to enjoy whatever sort of Christmas they could. The Centralia mine disaster in 1947 had killed one hundred and eleven miners, and the West Frankfort death list was one hundred nineteen. Despite strong agitation for stricter safety laws, including a Federal code with more than merely the right to suggest safety measures, nothing constructive had been done.

SPOTLIGHT ON CONGRESS
JANUARY 14, 1952

THE SEEMINGLY RESPECTABLE MINK

JANUARY 16, 1952

WASHINGTON scandals involving mink coats for wives of derelict officials got great play and that was easily understood. Far greater stakes were involved in tidelands oil, but it lacked the personal touch of a fur coat and the simplicity of a free deep freeze.

KING GEORGE VI of England died in his sleep on the night of February 5, 1952, at Sandringham. The crown passed to his daughter Elizabeth, first queen since Victoria. Two recent world wars and the changes they wrought gave Elizabeth a different realm from the famed Empire of the Victorian era. Austerity stalked the homeland and the old Empire was now a Commonwealth of Nations. India, "brightest jewel in the crown," was an independent state.

A DIFFERENT QUEEN—A DIFFERENT BRITAIN
FEBRUARY 7, 1952

215

PRESIDENTIAL elections were coming up in 1952 against a background of a world divided between communism and the free nations. America was now playing the leading role on the side of freedom because of her economic power and potential military resources. This responsibility in world affairs, a role the British had long been accustomed to, was new to us, and many of our citizens and political leaders still felt reluctant about assuming that task. Whether that important issue would be made clear to the voters or whether the campaign would be resolved on petty questions was in the lap of the gods. Nominating decisions made in smoke-filled rooms might mean much in 1952.

**A SMOKE-FILLED ROOM COULD MEAN
A SMOKE-FILLED WORLD**
FEBRUARY 24, 1952

TOWARD the end of March both parties were courting reluctant candidates who seemingly had no wish to run. Governor Stevenson was up for re-election in Illinois and wanted very much to carry on the reforms he had started in his first term following the inept Dwight Green administration. General Eisenhower, a professional soldier who had never been in politics, was still in uniform in Europe building the NATO defense organization.

THE THINKERS
MARCH 27, 1952

On March 29 at the Jefferson Day Dinner in Washington President Truman definitely withdrew from the race with this statement: "I shall not be a candidate for re-election; I shall not accept a renomination."

OUT ON THE OPEN RANGE
MARCH 31, 1952

Easter hats for both parties were by the same designer.

EASTER–'52
APRIL 13, 1952

OPENING CHORUS
JUNE 5, 1952

SENATOR Taft's candidacy had the backing of the hard core of old professional politicians, the big contributors and the Southern delegates. They took over every key position in the convention and were fully prepared to put the Eisenhower-Dewey group, or any stampeding amateurs, such as the 1940 Wilkie supporters in Philadephia, in their places. But the machine was too obvious in its operation. In 1920 it could nominate Harding in a smoke-filled hotel room, but in 1952 television brought the whole show before the eyes of millions of voters and the old pros lost the battle.

WHEN General Eisenhower was first mentioned as a Presidential possibility, it was not known whether he was a Democrat or a Republican or whether he would enter the race.

It turned out that the general was a Republican and would now accept that party's nomination. On June 5, he made his first major political address at a homecoming celebration at Abilene, Kansas.

ON TO CHICAGO!
JUNE 10, 1952

ALL SET

JUNE 16, 1952

AT THE CHICAGO STOCKYARDS

JULY 8, 1952

ONE PUNCH

JULY 12, 1952

ANYTHING CAN HAPPEN AT THE STOCKYARDS

JULY 13, 1952

AS THE CURTAIN GOES UP
JULY 20, 1952

THE Democratic show opened with no plot and a scattered cast of characters. President Truman had withdrawn from the lead role and Governor Stevenson refused to try for the part.

Since both conventions were held in the Chicago stockyards district, I felt it appropriate to preserve the packing-house atmosphere in the cartoons. At the Democratic meeting the clash between the Northern Liberals and the Southern Bourbons led the Donkey to the door, but not quite into the hash factory. The nomination of Stevenson and Sparkman, of Alabama, seemed to have spared the Donkey that fate—at least it appeared to at that time.

ALMOST GOT HIM IN
JULY 24, 1952

THE HAT-FILLED AIR
JULY 26, 1952

NOTHING IN IT FOR HIM

JULY 27, 1952

WITH Stevenson and Eisenhower heading the two major party tickets, it seemed certain the country couldn't lose. Both candidates represented, in the public mind, an enlightened outlook on foreign problems, and if Stalin were hoping for gains as a result of American elections he was doomed to be bitterly disappointed.

221

MEMBERS OF THE CAST
AUGUST 29, 1952

ABOUT a month later when the campaign actually got going it became apparent that the General's "crusade" was officered by some strange characters who did not seem to represent the ideals associated in the public mind with the Commander of the "crusade."

LEADERS of the Eisenhower movement in Texas attempted to rig the ballot by placing his name on the Democratic ticket. This failed because it was a little too raw. The Texas Republicans had taken over the entire list of state Democratic candidates and Eisenhower headed that ticket. These maneuvers smacked of a fraud on the sacred two-party system.

IN ANOTHER development, Colonel McCormick of the Taft army went "over the hill" and formed a Third Party.

THE TWO-FACED PARTY SYSTEM
AUGUST 31, 1952

FIRST YOU LAY AN EGG—
SEPTEMBER 4, 1952

OF 1,385 daily newspapers, 67.34% (with 80.24% of the total circulation) supported the Republican ticket in the 1952 campaign. They all favored the two-party political system, yet the press division was out of all proportion to the division of voters in the two major parties. It could better be compared with the proportion of Republican votes in the election to that of the Vegetarian Party. The serious implication of this disproportion lies in the charges that news of the campaign was unfairly handled.

Some of the country's leading newspapers declared for General Eisenhower for President months before the party nominating conventions and even before it was known whether he would be a candidate, or to which party, if any, he belonged.

The St. Louis *Post-Dispatch* reserved judgment until the candidates were named and their positions on the issues were made clear. The editorial order of the procedure, as I understood it, was to call the shots from day to day as we saw them. Most of my associates and I were favorably disposed toward Eisenhower. I had met the General on a couple of occasions and was as impressed with his personal charm as I had been by his distinguished war record. My editor, Irving Dilliard, had served under the general on his World War II staff at SHAEF in Europe. As a resident of Illinois, Editor Dilliard had written Eisenhower's name in on the ballot in the April primary election.

Because the *Post-Dispatch* eventually joined the meager ranks of the "loyal opposition" press, and because in some quarters the 1952 election was regarded as the end of another era, more space has been devoted to this election than was given to previous Presidential campaigns.

"EXTR-E-E, EXTR-E-E, ALL ABOUT TH' TWO-PARTY SYSTEM"
SEPTEMBER 9, 1952

THE IDEALS of the crusade soon faced the practical business of getting votes and winning the election. The lowest-level critics of General George C. Marshall, Eisenhower's great friend and mentor, were embraced.

The party machinery and big money contributors were controlled by .the defeated Taft. After the famous breakfast at Morningside Heights, terms were agreed upon by the politically experienced Senator and the General.

MEANWHILE, the brilliant wit of candidate Stevenson needled the crusade's contradictions, even through the elephant's tough hide. The reply was an insinuation that humor in a campaign verged on disloyalty.

LACKING a good joke book or a sense of humor, other resources were exploited.

OFF ON A STRANGE CRUSADE
SEPTEMBER 14, 1952

"CHINS UP NOW, AND CARRY ON"
SEPTEMBER 15, 1952

"NOW DON'T KID US; THIS IS SERIOUS!"
SEPTEMBER 17, 1952

PAY DIRT
SEPTEMBER 19, 1952

THE crusade had made a holy cause out of the "mess in Washington." It was slightly embarrassing when it was learned that the second in command, Vice-Presidential candidate Richard Nixon, was the beneficiary of a secret trust fund set up by wealthy supporters in California. This was not a campaign fund, but something to supplement the $75,000 a year the Senator received as salary and office expenses.

THE little corporal who had defeated the Taft forces in Chicago found himself supplanted by the very forces he had routed. "GENERAL" Taft seemed to be in command.

THE PRACTICAL MR. NIXON

SEPTEMBER 21, 1952

"WHY, WHERE HAVE YOU BEEN, DICKEY BOY?"

SEPTEMBER 23, 1952

SOJOURNING AT ELBA

SEPTEMBER 24, 1952

WON THE WAR AND LOST THE PEACE

OCTOBER 5, 1952

THIS IS THE ISSUE
SEPTEMBER 28, 1952

THIS cartoon accompanied a full-page editorial entitled "The Choice for President," in which the *Post-Dispatch* analyzed all the issues, point by point, and the positions taken by the candidates, and concluded by saying, "The independent voter, in our opinion, will serve the best interests of the country as a whole by voting for Adlai Stevenson for President."

228

HE KEPT HIS WORD

NOVEMBER 2, 1952

THIS was the final cartoon of the campaign, published on Sunday, November 2.

THE VERDICT
NOVEMBER 5, 1952

Govenor Stevenson maintained in defeat the same gallant good sense he displayed during the campaign. To the distressed party workers in Springfield, Illinois, he told this story:

> Someone asked me, as I came in down on the street, how I felt. I am reminded of a story that a fellow townsman of ours used to tell, Abraham Lincoln. When they asked him how he felt once after an unsuccessful election, he said he felt like a little boy who had stubbed his toe in the dark; that he was too old to cry but it hurt too much to laugh.

As a cub artist on the Chicago *Daily News*, I sketched notables at the GOP convention in 1912 when William Howard Taft was nominated and Teddy Roosevelt formed the Bull Moose, a third party. My first Presidential ballot was cast for T. R.

Of all the candidates for the Presidency I have ever voted for, none, in my opinion, measured up to the stature in every way of Adlai Stevenson, and I am proud to have had the opportuniy to support him and his cause.

For those who choose to discount a cartoonist's opinion, may I quote from a postelection editorial from the *Wall Street Journal*:

> The supporters of Mr. Stevenson have nothing to be ashamed of in him and much, we think, to be proud of. No man could have better stated the cause of his party; no man could have so well demonstrated that his is a party that can claim allegiance from men of stature.
>
> And not the least of the things Mr. Stevenson's supporters have to be proud of was what he said in his dark hour. His words, of course, were molded to a long tradition which accepts political defeat graciously, but those words also told of him that he understood the wisdom of that tradition. That which unites us is greater than that which divides us.
>
> With no sense of disparagement, but with a deep pride in the quality of men that this country can uncover in its crucial days, we think that nothing better revealed in Mr. Stevenson a quality for leadership than the manner of his yielding it.

230

NEW PILOT—WHAT COURSE?
NOVEMBER 9, 1952

THE world and America's new position in world affairs made the President-Elect something more than America's chief executive.

TOO BAD FOR YOU, JOE
NOVEMBER 16, 1952

DESPITE the personal differences developed during the campaign, President Truman, because of the critical situation in international affairs, invited President-Elect Eisenhower to the White House for a conference in order to bridge the gap between the November election and the January inauguration.

The meeting was arranged and General Eisenhower appointed cabinet members who could, by cooperating with the outgoing administration, familiarize themselves with the pressing and dangerous problems which could immobilize the outgoing administration, confuse our allies, and catch the new administration off balance.

The measure of this cooperation, prompted by the world-wide emergency, set a precedent in the transfer of power from one party to another in Washington.

IN UNCHARTED WATERS
NOVEMBER 19, 1952

WAITING FOR JANUARY 20
NOVEMBER 23, 1952

PRAYER FOR RAIN
NOVEMBER 9, 1952

THE Midwest endured serious drouth in 1952. Farmers naturally suffered, and woods and brush became so dry they burned like tinder. Fires destroyed many homes and thousands of acres of valuable timber, which, in the case of hardwoods, would take years to replace.

TRIAL IN CZECHOSLOVAKIA
NOVEMBER 21, 1952

THE FIRST cartoon on Czechoslovakia in this volume was published November 10, 1947. From that November to this November tragedy had stalked that unfortunate country. Under communist rule the Red slogan, "Worker's paradise," became "Hangman's paradise."

BRUSHING UP
NOVEMBER 30, 1952

THE LATEST purge revealed a new capital offense, Zionism. The new rulers of Russia were now back to the old Czars with new techniques learned along the way.

234

THERE GOES THE HONEYMOON
DECEMBER 4, 1952

DOMESTIC strife broke out early in the new Washington family. Senator Taft voiced heated objection to the appointment of Martin Durkin, Chicago, as Secretary of Labor. Back of his objection to that particular appointment was the realization that the rival Dewey faction had moved into the new cabinet in a big way.

SEARCH FOR A KEY
DECEMBER 5, 1952

PRESIDENT-ELECT Eisenhower followed up his campaign promise to visit Korea and seek at first hand an honorable solution to the struggle.

"HAPPY DAYS ARE HERE AGAIN"
DECEMBER 10, 1952

ON THE WAY home from Korea the President-elect and his party stopped off for a few days in Hawaii. Prospective Cabinet members were called in for a get-together meeting. Mr. Eisenhower had an opportunity to indulge in his favorite pastime, golf, and the G.O.P. elephant, out of power for twenty years, caught the spirit of the occasion.

237

CIVIL LIBERTIES
CIVIL RIGHTS

AS AMERICA GOES SO GOES THE WORLD
JANUARY 4, 1953

MOST Americans have become so accustomed to freedom they take it for granted. This is a dangerous attitude, especially at a time when freedom has few outposts in the world and when these outposts are being seriously challenged by dictators on both sides of the iron curtain.

President Eisenhower pointedly recognized this danger when he made freedom the principal theme of his inaugural address. There are no controls which automatically regulate the price of freedom and keep it in our grasp if we forget the old price formula of "eternal vigilance."

238